Well! You wonder ....
next! Can there be anything new or merely a rehash of previous subjects? <u>Not only is this new material and a new perspective</u>, but this book is one for you to hand out to pastors, elders, deacons, and any Christian who is serious about his faith!

> Jay E. Adams, Ph.D., Dean of the Christian Counseling
> and Educational Foundation

Dr. Payne's book combines two qualities that are often lacking in contemporary discussions of issues in medical ethics: firsthand medical expertise, and a sound, conservative Biblical theology. Not every reader will agree with his conclusions, but every reader has much to learn from this timely volume. I warmly recommend it to anyone who is looking for Biblical perspectives on these important issues facing the Church.

> John Jefferson Davis, Ph.D., Professor of Systematic
> Theology and Christian Ethics, Gordon-Conwell
> Theological Seminary

When confronted by the burning issues of our day, the Church has been too-long content to offer only generalities or echoes of liberalism garnished with Scripture. However, Dr. Ed Payne has found the Biblical passages which, when joined to medical data, lead to practical answers. That many of his views are not very close to medical orthodoxy reveals just how far medicine has strayed from its only proper basis: the Bible.

> Dr. Hilton Terrell, Ph.D., M.D., Editor, *Journal of*
> *Biblical Ethics in Medicine*

I have often known Ed Payne to be radical in his thinking about the issues of medicine and healing. I have never known him to be careless. You will be startled when you read this book, and you may end up disagreeing with certain points. But you had also better be prepared to think -- and to think hard.

> Joel Belz, Executive Editor, *World* magazine

Biblical Healing
for
Modern Medicine

**Choosing Life and Health or...
Disease and Death**

Franklin E. Payne, Jr.

Covenant Books

Biblical Healing for Modern Medicine

Edited by Carol H. Blair

Library of Congress Catalog Card Number: 93-71420
ISBN 0-9629876-1-1

Printed and Bound in the United States of America

Table of Contents

The Physician and His Practice
Some Words to the Medical Student

To Carol H. Blair

Dedicated woman of God, incisive writer, and valued friend

Acknowledgements

No author is able to acknowledge all those people who have both shaped his thoughts and made opportunities possible for him. There are the great authors and minds of the past (e.g., Abraham Kuyper and J. Gresham Machen) and of the present (e.g., Jay E. Adams and Gordon H. Clark).

There are the "opportunity-makers," whose roles are no less important. My wife, Jeanne, graciously contends and helps with the "homework" that I create with publishing projects. My daughter, Nikki, has done her share of the work, as well.

No editor could be more of a joy to work with than Carol Blair. She is both professional and prompt -- attributes that enable and enhance a writer's work. For her invaluable help to me and her commitment to God's truth, I happily dedicate this book to her.

Dr. Hilton Terrell is my "alter-ego" in the best sense of that expression. More than 15 years of collaboration, challenge, and review has taught me more than I would have ever learned without him.

Dr. Jay Adams is always there to help at a moment's notice and provides encouragement and counsel in a variety of ways.

Dr. Joe Tollison is a Chairman (of Family Medicine) who provides not only opportunity, but encouragement as well.

One of the greatest joys of the Christian life is the people who help make us be the best that we can be. To these and countless others, may God's richest blessings be yours!

Introduction

AIDS!

Acquired immunodeficiency syndrome.

It strikes fear into the hearts of people everywhere. Parents keep their children home from school. Dentists wear masks and gloves with their patients. Public health officials vigorously try to calm the public. Fundamentalists shout that AIDS is the wrath of God.

A newborn baby is found alive in the dirty laundry of a hospital delivery suite. Children are found playing in the streets with "dolls" that turn out to be the bodies of aborted babies. "Women's clinics" are bombed and picketed. Politicians debate whether abortion will split the nation as did the issue of slavery.

News bulletin! The President of the United States is shot by a young man trying to attract the attention of an idolized actress who will pay him no attention. Is he a criminal? No! He is only "sick" and is placed in a hospital.

What is going on here? These events are hardly the routine practice of medicine. Yet, they illustrate the practice of modern medicine, and they are characteristic products of our American culture.

"AIDS is not a moral problem, it is a medical problem." ("They" say.) "We must not make moral judgments about homosexuals and IV-drug abusers" (even though these two groups account for more than 90 percent of adults who are infected with AIDS). "What everyone should do is learn to practice 'safe sex' and the drug users be given 'free' sterile needles and syringes. These are the solutions, for the problems are medical, not moral!" ("They" say.)

What about abortion? What is it? The largest medical organization in the United States, the American Medical Association, defends the current practice of abortion. In an official brief before the Supreme Court, the AMA called abortion "sound medical practice."

John Hinckley, the young man who shot former President Reagan, is an example of the concept of "mental illness" at its extreme distortion of personal responsibility. "The mentally ill are not morally responsible for their actions. The 'problem' is something outside their control. Something is wrong with the chemicals that make up their body. Something is wrong with other people -- especially their parents who raised them" (an anti-family position). "They need to be taken away from the 'pressures' of job and family and put where they can talk openly with someone who will give them 'unconditional love.'" ("They" say.)

While some Christians perceive these three problems as I have presented them, many do not. Many perceive them as though they are isolated examples. What we must face, however, is that the whole practice of medicine is influenced by the same disorientation. *The whole practice of medicine has become anti-Christian and anti-Biblical.* It is not just a few isolated practices that need to be examined closely from a Biblical perspective, but *everything* about modern medicine.

The above practices are the consistent application of a philosophy that is based upon godless evolution and secular humanism. Such practices have steadily infiltrated American thinking for decades and have now arrived. But -- I want to direct our attention more specifically. *Medicine is inherently religious.*[1] Its practice is inseparable from religious beliefs, and those practices are determined by the beliefs of its practitioners.

The central problem is that Christians continue to consider that medicine and faith are separate moral categories (except for the categories of the saved and the unsaved). This book aims to correct that false conception. This goal cannot be reached, however, unless it is crystal clear that *everything* in our everyday lives is religious. Every thought and every incidental act is religious. *And not for Christians only!* Everything that everyone does is religious.

The problem is that religion is usually associated with some belief about the "supernatural." That is, reality exists that is above and beyond man's senses. For example, Muslims believe the Koran and pray toward Mecca. Primitive tribesmen paint themselves and dance in frenzy to appease their gods.

But what about the atheist? He does not believe in a god or anything that he cannot perceive with his five senses. Is he religious? Most definitely, he is!

The denial of anything supernatural is religious because it is a belief about the supernatural. You see, no belief can avoid a supernatural position. Everyone must either believe that something supernatural exists or that it doesn't. *Thus, a personal religion is unavoidable for everyone.*

Are you aware that the Supreme Court has called humanism and atheism religions? (Sometimes, albeit rarely, the High Court thinks clearly!) Not that the Supreme Court is the final judge of what is and what is not a religion. Their rulings, however, agree with the concept that these "-isms" are indeed religions, even though they believe in nothing supernatural.

A better way to think about this subject is that each person has personal beliefs about reality and how people should behave in light of that reality. That is their religion. Christians might make more progress in their debates over prayer and creationism in the schools if we argued that these issues represent different religious views. The decision is not *whether* to have religion in the schools, but *which* religion.

The decision is not that the practice of medicine should be non-religious, but *which religion*. You believe in prayer. Will your physician pray with you? If he will not, does his omission limit his medical effectiveness? Could his "fervent prayer" as "a righteous man" enhance his care for you (James 5:16)?

You believe that parents are responsible for their children. Will your physician give birth control pills to children (perhaps your own) and treat them for sexually transmitted diseases (the modern euphemism for "venereal diseases") without your consent? (It is legal for physicians to treat minors for these two "medical" problems in every state in the United States.)

You believe that "not bearing false witness" is God's commandment. Will your physician lie to his patients or to you?

You believe, "You shall not murder," but will your physician give you or a member of your family something to "end suffering" permanently?

You believe that Christ is the "only way," but is your physician promoting certain methods (such as Transcendental Meditation, acupuncture, and reflexology) along with Eastern religious practices?[2] Many physicians are.

Now, *is medicine religious or not*? Certainly it is! The question is, "Which religion will determine how medicine is practiced?"

A System of Death

Modern medicine is often touted as promoting health and long life. In many ways, however, it is *a system of death*.

What is the solution for "inconvenient" pregnancies? The unborn child is put to *death*, even beyond the time when he could be kept alive outside the womb!

What is the solution for defective babies? Treatment is simply withheld until they *die*.

How can suffering be ended for chronically or terminally ill patients? They can be *killed* directly or *allowed to die* by failing to initiate or by withholding treatment.

What is the result of physicians' endorsement of sexual immorality? The most obvious and serious is AIDS, the present and future cause of hundreds of thousands of *deaths*.

Less obvious, but perhaps just as serious when they are considered as a whole, are over twenty other sexually transmitted diseases. These are serious diseases that cause disability and *death*. Disabilities include sterility, ectopic pregnancies, spontaneous miscarriage of future pregnancies, intestinal obstruction, and severe, recurring pain. These diseases have virtually exploded in numbers over the past 20 years, coincidental with the idea of sexual "freedom." This *freedom*, however, has turned out to be *bondage* to these ongoing physical problems.

Less directly, the endorsement of immorality contributes to the *death* of the family. Extensive research shows that married people are more healthy and live longer than those who are never-married, divorced or widowed.[3] In many cases, the infertility that often results from sexually transmitted diseases actually prevents even *the existence of future families with children.* Anything that is anti-family is unhealthy, and in the long run, causes the *death* of individuals, their personal families, *and their posterity*!

Wait a minute, you say! If modern medicine is a death system, why has life expectancy increased so dramatically in the United States? The fact is, life expectancy has not increased for everyone, and the associated statistics are seriously distorted. The explanation goes back to religious beliefs.

If aborted babies are calculated into a prediction of life expectancy, life expectancy from the time of conception is reduced to 43 years! With the zeros (for *no* life expectancy) of 1.5 million aborted babies each year in the United States factored into 2.0 million deaths from other causes (heart attacks, strokes, cancer, etc.), it is easily seen how abortion affects true life expectancy.

Perhaps no illustration can better contrast and underscore the importance of definitions. So, instead of increasing longevity, "sound medical practice" has decreased it to 43 years, less than what it was before 1900 in the United States, and less than what it currently is in underdeveloped countries that do not practice abortion!

Throughout this book we will explore other ways in which modern medicine directly or indirectly promotes this "death system" as a result of its failure to recognize the Lordship of Jesus Christ and His Word.

The Major Hurdle: Facing Medical Reality

I fear that the major hurdle to a truly Biblical ethic in medicine is the myth of the effectiveness of modern medicine. (See Chapter 3.) Reality can be perceived only when myths are destroyed. That is not to say that everything in medicine should be thrown out. Some things, as we have discussed, and will discuss, must be discarded. Other things are not as obvious, and we must reason together to discover their effectiveness and their "fit" within a Biblical ethic.

All I ask of the reader for the moment is to take medicine off the pedestal where it has been placed by our culture. Thus removed, we can place the authority of God and His Word in its place, evaluate what we are doing, and construct an approach to medicine that is pleasing to God and that fully promotes the health of all people.

There are two compelling reasons for this approach. First and foremost, Christians must "highly exalt" Christ in medicine, as one dimension of His authority "*...in heaven, and on earth, and under the earth" (Philippians 2:10, NASB).* Second, *there is no other approach* that is truly "wholistic." That is, only a full and thorough application of God's instructions for man will result in maximal health for individuals and societies.

Notes and References

1. I am aware that many Christians believe that Christianity is not a religion. Within proper philosophical definitions, however, *Christianity is a religion*, even though it is unique in its means of salvation, its Savior, its Book, and its God. Philosophers may debate with such terms as first principles, axioms, presuppositions, premises, etc., but that approach uses only *uncommon* terms to define the basis of those choices that are *common* (everyday) and that determine our behaviors, even though these principles may not be well-defined in the minds of those who hold them.

2. Samuel Pfieffer, *Healing at Any Price?: The Dangers of Alternative Medicine* (Milton Keynes, England: Word Publishers, 1988); Paul C. Reisser, Teri K. Reisser, and John Weldon, *New Age Medicine: A Christian Perspective on Holistic Health* (Downers Grove, Illinois: InterVarsity Press, 1987).

3. James J. Lynch, *The Broken Heart: The Medical Consequences of Loneliness* (New York: Basic Books, 1977).

CHAPTER 1

True Wholistic Health:
A Sound Mind and a Sound Body

"Is anyone among you sick? Let him call for the elders of the church, and let them pray over him, anointing him with oil in the name of the Lord. And the prayer of faith will save the sick, and the Lord will raise him up. And if he has committed sins, he will be forgiven. Confess your trespasses to one another, and pray for one another, that you may be healed. The effective, fervent prayer of a righteous man avails much" (James 5:14-16).

Poor first-century Christians! Spiritually, they had the vitality of a new faith, but physically, they did not have the treatments of modern medicine to cure their diseases.

Medicine was not "scientific," as it is today. Physicians had few medicines and little surgery, and they were often indentured servants. Treatments by modern standards were crude and only a few could possibly have worked. A patient might get leeches from one physician and potions from another.

Of course, some Christians had Luke, the beloved physician and companion of Paul (Colossians 4:14). They were the fortunate ones who had the services of a most knowledgeable physician and believer!

Except -- there is no passage in the New Testament in which Luke treated anyone, much less effected a cure!

In fact, all the cures in the entire Bible were miraculous, and never came from the ministrations of a physician.

Does that mean we should never consult a physician? Should we seek only miraculous healing?

The answer to both questions is "No." What we must do first is understand health from a Biblical perspective and *then* incorporate modern medical practices into that understanding.

Soul and Body

Modern medicine considers man to be an animal who evolved from a primordial soup. He has no characteristics that animals do not have, only "higher" functions. He is simply an orderly arrangement of biochemicals, and at death he ceases to exist. These views belong to your own physician unless he believes in a religion (e.g., Christianity, Judaism,and Islam) which holds that existence continues after this life.

The Bible, however, states that man is made in the image of God (see Genesis 1:26-27), in contrast to the animals, who are not. Furthermore, God "... *formed man of the dust of the ground, and breathed into his nostrils the breath of life; and man became a living being" (Genesis 2:7)*. More specifically, in this context, *being* is *soul* (see KJV).

Thus, man is both body and soul. He is made of the "dust of the ground" (the physical component), but more importantly, God also made him with a *soul* (the nonphysical component).

We could easily get sidetracked here with two issues. First, the specific contributions of the body and of the soul to all that man is and does could be discussed. The specific identities of those roles, however, are not necessary to our task here. What must be recognized for a Biblical understanding of health and medicine is that man is composed of two elements: body and soul. They form a whole. Both must be healthy for Biblical health, and both must be "treated" in the practice of Biblical medicine.

Second, we could get sidetracked with the dichotomy/trichotomy issue. That is, is man composed of body and soul (spirit) or body, soul, and spirit? A discussion of these two positions, however, is not necessary at this time. *The crucial factor is to recognize that man does have a nonphysical component.* Whether this nonphysical side is one part or two parts does not matter in our current context. In the area of psychiatry and psychology, the problem becomes more important, but we will deal with that issue in Chapter 5.

I will use *soul* and *spirit* as synonyms in order to keep our discussion more simple. The Bible presents them as the same, but viewed from different relationships to the body. The *soul* is often used to designate the whole person or the nonphysical component of man in close association with the body. The *spirit* designates the nonphysical component in its functions that are not closely related to the body.

But, what is the importance of these two elements? *"For bodily exercise profits a little, but godliness is profitable for all things, having promise of the life that now is and of that which is to come" (I Timothy 4:8).*

This verse sets the proper perspective. *The health of the spirit (godliness) is far more important than the health of the body.* To understand health and medical practice Biblically, this principle is central and basic.

Some Christians have ignored this basic principle. They have used this verse to champion bodily exercise far out of proportion to needed emphasis on spiritual applications. While this verse *does* give credence to the "profit" from exercise, from my observations as a physician and as a counselor, most Christians are in far greater need of the spiritual applications than of bodily exercise. Don't misread me. I am in print and have talked about the value of exercise. I run 10-15 miles a week and work out with weights. Paul's emphasis here, however, is our spiritual condition. *His emphasis is our greatest need!* In this chapter and in the remainder of the book, we will explore in some detail the measures that promote physical *and* spiritual health.

The verses with which we began this chapter illustrate. The Greek word *sozo*, translated "save" (the sick, James 5:15), is the most common one for salvation in the New Testament. It is used, for example, in Matthew 1:21, John 3:17, and Romans 5:9. It is the word from which we derive the English word *soteriology*, "the study of the doctrine of salvation." Here in James, however, the reference is to the person who is sick, with the implication that he will be healed. The New International Version reads "make the sick person well," and the New American Standard Bible reads "restore the one who is sick."

Which is it? Does the passage mean healing of the body, or salvation of the soul? It can mean either or both!

To develop this meaning fully, we must go back a long way. In fact, all the way to the "beginning."

Adam and Eve Disobey

"And the Lord God commanded the man, saying, 'Of every tree of the garden you may freely eat; but of the tree of the knowledge of good and evil you shall not eat, for in the day that you eat of it you shall surely die'" (Genesis 2:16-17).

After God had created Adam and Eve, He called everything "very good" (Genesis 1:31). Everything was in perfect order. There was no sin *and no disease* on the earth. Adam and Eve were to commune with God and live forever, never knowing disease or ill health.

Then -- Disaster! Death! Disease! Expulsion from the Garden!

Why?

Sin.

Adam and Eve disobeyed, and God, as He always does, fulfilled His promise. The *issue* is sin. The *result* is God's punishment. Sin and punishment are the cause of disease and death. The cure is Jesus Christ, Whose correction of this disaster was promised immediately after Adam and Eve's sin: *"He shall bruise your head, and you shall bruise His heel" (Genesis 3:15).* We know from our New Testament understanding that this text meant that Jesus Christ would be wounded by Satan ("bruise His heel" -- a nonfatal injury), but that He would totally defeat Satan, sin, and death ("bruise your head" -- a fatal injury).

The Most Basic Issue Is Salvation

Thus, *the most basic issue concerning disease and death is salvation*. The Biblical position is that health includes both soul and body. One Greek word, *hugies*, used for healing in the New Testament, is identified with our English word *hygiene*. It refers to what is clearly physical healing, as in *"It was restored as 'whole' as the other" (Matthew 12:13).* It also clearly refers to healing that is spiritual, as in *"those (sinners) who are 'sick'"* *(Luke 5:31).*

This spiritual prerequisite for health is often missed by both Christians and non-Christians. *Anyone who is not saved by Jesus Christ cannot be considered to be healthy.* Any Christian who speaks of health without understanding and communicating that salvation in Christ is basic to total (wholistic) health is not presenting a Biblical position. *Someone who is not a Christian is not healthy,* no matter what his physical condition.

Two serious consequences occur when this position is not recognized or presented clearly. First, the unbeliever will not understand this need in his life. If he thinks that he can be healthy without Christ, why does he need Him?

Second, and equally serious, there is no distinction between the concept of health and medicine for the Christian and the non-Christian. This is the difficult situation in which we now find ourselves: The practice of medicine is (regrettably and wrongly) little different for the Christian and the non-Christian.

The word *salvation,* however, needs more explanation. Christians are too often vague as to what salvation means. They would do well to study the various aspects of salvation. For example, one text mentions five parts: foreknowledge, predestination, calling, justification, and glorification (see Romans 8:29-30). These parts are not all there are, but this verse indicates that salvation has many definite parts.

We focus on two parts: regeneration (Titus 3:5) and sanctification (I Thessalonians 4:3). *Regeneration* is the "change of heart" that converts a person from an enemy of God (Romans 5:10) to a child of God (John 1:12). The evidence of regeneration is *sanctification,* or more specifically, *obedience.* Again, *"For this is the will of God, your sanctification" (I Thessalonians 4:3).* Our sanctification is our obedience to God's Word. Also, our sanctification, as obedience, demonstrates our love for God (see John 14:15, 21).

The point is, salvation results in such a definite change in the pattern of one's life that it cannot be missed. It is a "new creation" (II Corinthians 5:17).

It is this definitive lifestyle that most fully promotes health in this earthly life. Your Bible study, church attendance, prayers, fellowship, and exercise of your spiritual gift(s) (and every other way that we are to obey God) promote both your spiritual and your physical health. (See Appendix 2.)

It seems that many Christians give more attention to nutrition, exercise, and other health practices more than they do to these spiritual exercises. Biblically, however, spiritual disciplines are far more important for health than those that affect only the body (I Timothy 4:8).

Thus, the Christian health-care worker must not only manage physical behaviors that promote health, but spiritual attitudes and behaviors, as well. *If he doesn't, he is simply not promoting Biblical health.* And, as we will see, he will not be able to make diagnoses of spiritual conditions that cause physical problems. That is, he will not be practicing Biblical medicine. We will examine these "covert" contributions to disease later in the chapter.

Hard Questions

1) Are all physical diseases and death due to sin? 2) If Jesus Christ is the answer, shouldn't all Christians be free from disease? 3) If sin is the problem, should we use physicians at all?

The answer to the first question is "Yes" and "No."

Yes, all disease is directly the result of the sin *of Adam and Eve.* No, all disease is not directly the result of the personal sin of the one afflicted. Yes, much disease is the result of personal sin. Yes, the most important factor for health is salvation. We will explore this matter further in the next section.

The answer to the second question is "No." It seems obvious, with all the health problems that Christians have. Yet, many Christians actually teach that we should be free of disease. Because of the importance and complexity of the issue, we will leave this discussion for Chapter 10.

The answer to the third question is a qualified "Yes." As we saw in the Introduction, physicians cannot be given *carte blanche* to use any and all treatments. They clearly practice gross immorality in some areas. This entire book will present what physicians should and should not do and give direction for further definition of the role of Christian physicians.

Now, let us look more closely at these issues.

The Causes of Disease and Death: Overt

All disease and death is the result of the sin of Adam and Eve. Disease and death, however, may or may not be a result of the personal sin of the person afflicted.

"Now as Jesus passed by, He saw a man who was blind from birth. And His disciples asked Him, saying, 'Rabbi, who sinned, this man or his parents, that he was born blind?' Jesus answered, 'Neither this man nor his parents sinned, but that the works of God should be revealed in him'" (John 9:1-3). Then, Jesus healed him.

All injury and death is not the personal punishment of sin either. *"There were present at that season some who told Him about the Galileans whose blood Pilate had mingled with their sacrifices. And Jesus answered and said to them, 'Do you suppose that these Galileans were worse sinners than all other Galileans, because they suffered such things? I tell you, no; but unless you repent you will all likewise perish. Or those eighteen on whom the tower in Siloam fell and killed them, do you think that they were worse sinners than all other men who dwelt in Jerusalem? I tell you, no; but unless you repent you will all likewise perish'" (Luke 13:1-5).*

Modern examples are harder to give. With our incomplete understanding we may not know the relationship between a disease or injury and sin. We can, however, mention a few examples that seem to be mostly or entirely unrelated to sin: breast cancer, various bone tumors, multiple sclerosis, congenital heart disease, brain tumors, cataracts, diabetes mellitus (insulin-dependent), and childhood asthma. Of course, sin can be implicated in some aspects of these, but the subject becomes more complex than what we are able to explore here. Some relationship of sin to sickness will be seen later.

Much disease, injury, and death, however, is due directly to the personal sins of the one afflicted or to others. To the man who was lowered through the roof because there was no other way to get him into His presence, Jesus said, *"Your* sins *are forgiven you," and the man was healed* (see Luke 5:17-26). Also, to the man at the pool of Bethesda, Jesus said, *"See, you have been made well. Sin no more, lest a worse thing come upon you"* (see John 5:1-15).

Because of the lack of detail in these passages, we cannot know for sure that each man had diseases or deformities that were entirely related to their sin, or not related at all. The implication, however, is that there was a significant cause-and-effect relationship between their sin and their sickness, because Jesus focused on their sin, not on their physical problems.

Modern examples are quite numerous in the United States. One-third of all cancer deaths are related to the use of tobacco. Lung cancer, the most frequent of these cancers, is the fourth most common cause of death. Cirrhosis of the liver, mostly caused by alcohol, is the sixth most common cause of death. Cancer of the cervix, one of the most common cancers in women, is now considered to be a sexually transmitted disease (STD). A common form of liver infection, hepatitis B, also falls into this category. AIDS, of course, is causing tens of thousands of deaths each year, and almost all cases are directly or indirectly caused by sexual immorality.

From these statistics, it would not be an overstatement to say that most current causes of disease, disability, and death are due directly to personal sin. Even if they are not "most," they are certainly a major part of these problems. For example, various organs, such as the heart, brain, and kidneys, just gradually "wear out" in the aging process. This gradual deterioration, however, may be rapidly accelerated by a failure to observe basic health and nutritional needs of the body.

Thus, we can see the balance that needs to be maintained. On the one hand, certain medical problems, as far as we can understand, are unrelated to sin. On the other hand, the most common problems that are managed by physicians today *are* sin-related. Clearly, these medical problems cannot be discussed or treated without reference to sin.

The Causes of Disease and Death: Covert

The New Testament pictures the life of a Christian as one that is disciplined and dynamic, yet orderly, and with a sense of peace.

"Discipline yourself for the purpose of godliness" (I Timothy 4:7, NASB) denotes this type of life, as Paul uses the Greek word *gumnazo*, the same word from which we get our word *gymnasium*. The implication of rigorous training and discipline is clear.

The "power" of the Holy Spirit is another common description of the Christian's life in the New Testament (Romans 15:13, II Corinthians 12:9, II Timothy 1:7). (The Greek word for "power" is commonly translated as "strength," also.)

"Self-control" (Galatians 5:23) and "sound mind" (II Timothy 1:7) are other words that imply orderliness of life and clarity of mind.

The "peace" of the Christian was clearly stated by Jesus Himself: *"Peace I leave with you, My peace I give to you; not as the world gives do I give to you. Let not your heart be troubled, neither let it be afraid" (John 14:27).*

Of course, these are not the only characteristics of the Christian and his or her life. They are, however, representative of a distinct lifestyle. It is this lifestyle that promotes health.

Irregular or overloaded schedules are stressful. Irregular sleep patterns prevent the full benefit of sleep. Unresolved conflicts in personal relationships cause tension and other physiological changes. Worry and anxiety trigger hormonal responses that may be harmful.

These changes weaken the body's defenses against infection and disease. In the presence of these stresses, a person often contracts a disease that he would not have otherwise contracted.

Furthermore, these stresses may cause bodily symptoms of disease when none is present. They may cause carelessness, leading to accidents that would not otherwise occur. Then, the focus and attention is given to the injury, and the cause is virtually ignored.

You may have gone to your physician when he ordered a

number of "tests," only to have him report to you later that they were all "normal"! Those symptoms for which you went to see him were likely due to stresses of this sort.

When King David sinned, he experienced severe physical symptoms.

> *"There is no soundness in my flesh*
> *Because of Your anger,*
> *Nor is there any health in my bones*
> *Because of my sin.*
> *For my iniquities have gone over my head;*
> *Like a heavy burden they are too heavy for me.*
> *My wounds are foul and festering*
> *Because of my foolishness" (Psalm 38:3-5).*

The Proverbs have many verses that clearly link righteousness with health, and sinfulness with illness. For example, consider these:

> *"Hope deferred makes the heart sick,*
> *But when the desire comes, it is a tree of life" (13:12).*

> *"A sound heart is life to the body,*
> *But envy is rottenness to the bones" (14:30).*

> *"A merry heart makes a cheerful countenance, But by*
> *sorrow of the heart the spirit is broken" (15:13).*

> *"The light of the eyes rejoices the heart,*
> *And a good report makes the bones healthy" (15:30).*

Elsewhere, the Bible often connects the health of the spirit with the health of the body. In some cases, symptoms are present without disease. In other cases, the stress causes a real disease in the body.

I fear that the most prevalent physical symptoms among Christians have to do with these subtle causes with or without disease. True believers are not often involved in gross immorality, but they do have disorderly and stressful lives. The actions most conducive to health are not necessarily nutrition and exercise, but establishing a greater degree of harmony and order in our homes and daily lives.

Let's take one example -- the Sabbath (i.e., Sunday). From the beginning, God intended one day a week to be one of rest (see Genesis 2:1-3). He considered this day so important that He made the observance of it one of the Ten Commandments (see Exodus 20:8-10). The violation of the Sabbath was one of the most common sins that God pointed out to the Israelites (see Numbers 15:32-36; Nehemiah 13:15-22; Jeremiah 17:19-27; Ezekiel 20:12-24). An entire chapter of the New Testament also speaks about the Sabbath (Hebrews 4).

Almost all of Christendom recognizes Sunday as the Sabbath under the New Covenant. Is it a day of rest for you? Or, is it a day of activity as frenzied as any other day of the week? Is the entire day one of rest and worship, including reading, reflecting and meditating on God's Word, except for engaging in acts of mercy (Matthew 12:9-14)? To honor God and the Sabbath has the secondary effect of your own spiritual and physical health. To "work" on Sunday is to cause the opposite.

All the ways in which Christians should change their thinking and behavior into Biblical patterns is too broad a subject to cover here. Jay Adams has written the most practical descriptions of these practices. These are detailed in *The Christian Counselor's Manual*.[1] (A more appropriate title for his book might be, "The Practical Guide to the Christian Life.") He has numerous other books on specific problems. Although many are written for pastors and counselors, that fact should not preclude your study of the Biblical principles in his books and their application to your own life. *Few other pursuits will promote your general health to such an extent.*

Conclusion: James 5:14-18

We now have the Biblical perspective to understand the verses in James with which we began this chapter. The one "sick" (Greek, *asthenes*, v. 14) may be sick of body, sick of spirit, or both. Elsewhere in the New Testament, this root denotes sickness of body (John 5:5; Acts 4:9; II Corinthians

12:5) or sickness of spirit (Romans 8:26; I Corinthians 8:7; Galatians 4:13). One passage clearly links a physical problem to a spiritual problem: Luke 13:10-13!

The sick person in James 5:14, then, may be a person who has a physical problem, a spiritual problem, or both. Thus, *"raise him up"* (v. 15) may refer to healing of the body, or healing of the spirit, or both. The conditional phrase "if he has committed sins" (v. 15), allows for illness that may or may not include the need for repentance. In some cases, repentance is all that will be needed!

Keen discernment in these situations is essential. The elders along with physicians will have to sort out what is spiritual and what is physical. Sometimes this task will be easy; sometimes it will be difficult; and sometimes, it will be impossible.

Thus, the designation of elders (or church leaders by other names -- for example, deacons in some Baptist churches) is important because these men should have this necessary discernment, if they were selected according to the Biblical criteria for that office (see I Timothy 3; Titus 1). That the practice of anointing with oil is rarely carried out does not negate God's instruction. A thorough understanding of medicine is not necessary. If John Wesley in 1759 could make the following observation, then modern elders should be able to do the same.[2]

> "... The care of a poor woman who had continued pain in her stomach.... They (physicians) prescribe drug upon drug without knowing a jot of the matter concerning the root of the disorders.... They cannot cure.... Whence came this woman's pain? (which she would never have told, had she never been questioned about it) -- from fretting for the death of her son.
>
> "Why then do not all physicians consider how far bodily disorders are caused or influenced by the mind, and in those cases, which are utterly out of their sphere, call in the assistance of a minister? . . . But why are these cases out of their sphere? Because they know not God. It follows, no man can be a thorough physician without being an experienced Christian."

It should be apparent that a non-Christian physician cannot be spiritually discerning. That is, *a non-Christian physician cannot practice true (Biblical) wholistic medicine.* Yet, many Christians see no reason to prefer a Christian physician over one who is not a Christian.

Of course, Christian physicians who can diagnose spiritually as well as physically are rare. Because so few Christian physicians fall into this category, a specific goal of this book is to increase the number who are willing to be trained in such discernment.

CHAPTER SUMMARY

1. Man is a unity of body and spirit.
2. Biblically, wholistic medicine must involve both body and spirit.
3. Perfect health was experienced by Adam and Eve prior to their sin and will be experienced by believers in Heaven.
4. Since man remains under the curse in a sinful world, perfect health is not possible on earth.
5. Health and healing may be maximized by an understanding and application of Biblical and medical knowledge, although Biblical knowledge has primary importance.
6. The most important factor in health is one's spiritual condition.
7. Maximal health is not possible for the unbeliever, because his spirit remains "sick" -- apart from regeneration and sanctification in Jesus Christ.
8. God's will for some Christians (for example, missionaries and martyrs) may not be physical health.
9. Non-Christian physicians cannot practice wholistic medicine.
10. The most common medical problems in the United States are directly caused or aggravated by sinful practices.
11. All sickness and injury is caused either by personal sin, the sins of others, the sin of Adam and Eve, or God's sovereign plan.
12. Health is primarily the responsibility of the individual and family and not that of the medical profession.

13. The practice of medicine may not violate Biblical principles to promote physical health.
14. Elders have a specific role in the illnesses of those in their "flock" to discern what possible role sin might play in those illnesses.

Notes and References

1. Jay E. Adams, *The Christian Counselor's Manual* (Grand Rapids: Baker Book House, 1975).

2. P. L. Parker (ed.), *The Journal of John Wesley* (Chicago: Moody Press, 1974), pp. 230-231.

CHAPTER 2

The Bible and the Practice of Medicine

"And in the thirty-ninth year of his reign, Asa became diseased in his feet, and his malady was very severe; yet in his disease he did not seek the Lord, but the physicians. So Asa rested with his fathers; he died in the forty-first year of his reign" (II Chronicles 16:12-13).

Asa made a mistake -- a bad mistake!

It cost him his life.

Immediately, we might conclude, "I will not make the same mistake; I will seek the Lord and not physicians." But -- our decision is not that simple. Asa's problem was not a wrong choice of healers.

Asa's primary problem was his turning from the Lord over a period of time. In the early years of his reign, he was one of the most righteous kings of Judah, after Israel had become a divided kingdom (and after King Solomon's death). He instituted many reforms and destroyed the worship of other gods (see II Chronicles 14:2-8; 15:12-19). When threatened by the Ethiopians, he called out *to the Lord* and was victorious (see II Chronicles 14:9-15).

For some reason, however, when threatened by Baasha, king of Israel, he sought the help of the king of Syria rather than God (II Chronicles 16:1-5).[1] God sent Hanani, a seer, to confront Asa on this issue, but Asa became angry and put Hanani in prison (see II Chronicles 16:7-10). Furthermore, he had begun to oppress his people (see II Chronicles 16:10b), when he had previously led them in righteousness (above).

Thus, Asa's failure to seek the healing of the Lord was only one more example of his departure from the Lord. We cannot use his experience as a proof text for the avoidance of physicians by Christians. Neither can we say that the virtual absence of effective medicine (from our modern vantage) was another reason that he should have "sought the Lord" rather than physicians.

Should Christians Seek the Care of Physicians?

Too often, Christians begin the discussion of a subject without first examining *what the Bible actually says* about it. Medicine surely must be one clear example of this failure! To my knowledge, no search had ever been done to determine what the Bible actually says about physicians, health, and healing, until I did the research for *Biblical/Medical Ethics* (published in 1985). Here, we will abbreviate and slightly alter that approach. (The entire text is Appendix 1 of this book.)

The word *physician* (Greek, *iatros*) appears four times in the Old Testament. We have already reviewed the most prominent text. Elsewhere, Egyptian physicians embalmed Jacob (Genesis 50:2); Job calls his accusers "worthless physicians" (Job 13:4); and Jeremiah calls for spiritual healing of the sins of Israel (Jeremiah 8:22). Yet, nothing is really present in these passages from which principles can be determined.

In the New Testament, *physician* appears seven times, with six of them being used by Jesus, and the other in reference to "Luke, the beloved physician" (see Colossians 4:14 and my Introduction). Three occur in the same context in parallel passages (Matthew 9:12, Mark 2:17, and Luke 5:31). Our Lord was challenged about His involvement with "tax collectors and sinners" and responded, *"... Those who are well do not need a physician, but those who are sick. I have not come to call the righteous, but sinners, to repentance" (Luke 5:31-32).*

Spiritual, rather than physical health is the focus of this passage, because Jesus specifies "sinners" as those who need a physician, that is, Himself, as the Great Physician.

Two other parallel passages use *physician* in a way that has a more direct bearing on the practice of medicine -- Mark 5:25

and Luke 8:43.

"Now a woman, having a flow of blood for twelve years, who had spent all her livelihood on physicians and could not be healed by any, came from behind and touched the border of His garment. And immediately her flow of blood stopped. And Jesus said, 'Who touched Me?' When all denied it, Peter and those with him said, 'Master, the multitudes throng You and press You, and You say, "Who touched me?" But Jesus said, 'Somebody touched Me, for I perceived power going out from Me.' Now when the woman saw that she was not hidden, she came trembling; and falling down before Him, she declared to Him in the presence of all the people the reason she had touched Him and how she was healed immediately. And He said to her, 'Daughter, be of good cheer; your faith has made you well. Go in peace'" (Luke 8:43-48).

This passage has some characteristics that are all too familiar to us today! She had spent her "livelihood" on physicians, indicating that medicine was not without its financial costs in those days. Also, she had not been helped, a common occurrence today (see Chapter 3). Finally, Jesus healed her. Yes, some healing does occur today, both miraculously and by physicians.

The word *physician* occurs in the last instance where Jesus quotes a proverb of His time: *"... Physician, heal yourself! ..."* *(Luke 4:23).* In the context, He is responding to the Jews to whom He had just identified Himself as the Messiah. Jesus, however, uses the expression as a rhetorical device and not as a principle of truth. Thus, it has no application to our search for principles concerning medical care.

In conclusion, all references to physicians in the Old and New Testaments give us no principles as to what the relationship of believers and the Church should be to physicians. But, to continue our Biblical search, we shall look at other references to health and healing.

Medical Practices in the Old Testament

The Old Testament contains much more about health and healing than does the New Testament, yet our review will be

brief. A great deal of work is needed to relate a modern understanding of health to the details of the Old Testament Law.
That effort is beyond our scope here.

The instructions that God gave to Israel included detailed
sanitation and infection control. A few examples follow.
Human waste was to be covered with dirt outside the camp (see
Deuteronomy 23:12-13). Priests were to examine people with
skin diseases (see Leviticus 13-14). (*Leprosy* was a term for a
variety of skin diseases that probably included what we now
call leprosy, but certainly was not limited to that one disease.)[2]
Dietary instructions were given (see Leviticus 11 and Deuteronomy 14). The management of certain kinds of "uncleanness"
was detailed (see Leviticus 15). Touching the dead was to be
avoided (see Numbers 19:11-22).

Some medical experts have been amazed that such "an-
cient" health laws were so "modern" in their separation of
infectious or potentially infectious people from others, and the
use of fire and water as disinfectants. Such practices were
unknown among the other nations of that time.[3] In fact, confir-
mation of these practices, relative to infectious agents, has been
known only for the last century -- a direct testimony of the
supernatural Source of such knowledge. Vigorous hand wash-
ing is now common procedure for all physicians, but there was
a time when it was a sign of distinction for physicians *not to
wash* after surgery or between patient examinations!

The question arises, however, as to whether these practices
were moral, civil, or ceremonial. That is, should they be practiced by Christians today, or were they a part of the Old Testament system that no longer applies because of Jesus Christ's
finished work? Actually, these measures involve all three
areas. Their separation is quite complex and, again, beyond
our focus here. It is, however, a work that needs to be done,
by physicians and theologians working together.

*Generally, however, these practices should be followed
today*. If God never contradicts Himself, then these practices
must have health benefits. There are only three possible positions regarding the Old Testament health laws: 1) These practices could have no health benefit (but that option is apparently
contradicted by modern medical understanding); 2) They could

have detrimental effects on health, but that would require God to have given unhealthy instructions to His people -- a contradiction of His character; or 3) They could have health benefits consistent with both spiritual and physical health. Clearly, the latter is the correct position, and it is supported by Scripture passages such as Deuteronomy 28:1-14; 30:15-20; and Joshua 1:7-8.

Even so, we must distinguish what practices are obligatory and what are not. These laws neither have merit for salvation nor have a high priority for Christians. The far greater health problems for both Christians and non-Christians are spiritual, rather than physical, as we discussed in the last chapter. That is the place to begin for the large majority of Christians. Then, they may become concerned with these particular practices.

In general, however, our Western society has sanitary measures that are consistent with many of these practices. Blood is drained from meat. Human waste is disposed "outside the camp" (sewage system). Persons with infectious diseases are quarantined. Most male children are circumcised. Thorough cleanliness in public eating places is required by law.

Medical Practices in the New Testament

Occasionally in the New Testament, "medicines" are used, but not by physicians. The twelve disciples "anointed" with some type of oil in their early ministry with Jesus (see Mark 6:13). The elders of the local church are to anoint (same Greek word as the verse in Mark) with oil (James 5:14). Most likely, however, these passages refer to ceremonial anointing rather than medicinal, because the context of each has more to do with a spiritual ministry of healing than expected effects of the medicines themselves. (I have analyzed this passage in James at some length in another book.)[4]

Paul directed Timothy, *"No longer drink only water, but use a little wine for your stomach's sake and your frequent infirmities"* (I Timothy 5:23). Why Paul gave this instruction is not clear. It is also not pertinent to our quest here, because Paul was not a physician.[5]

The Good Samaritan applied both oil and wine (see Luke

10:34). Again, the reason is unclear. This method may have been the common remedy of the day. It does not, however, instruct us concerning physicians, as these "remedies" were not directed or applied by a physician.

And so our review of physicians and medicinal remedies in Scripture is complete. It is apparent that we cannot derive principles from these passages. Other passages, however, as we will see, do apply.

Of more than passing interest is the fact that *every recorded instance of healing in the entire Bible is miraculous!* Even the practices of Luke, "the beloved physician," are not mentioned, yet Luke wrote the books of Luke and Acts. However, there is relevance for this absence of Biblical principle concerning physicians and medicines, as we will now investigate.

Medicine Is Inherently Religious

Most likely, Christians are never instructed in the Bible to see physicians for their medical care, because medical care is inherently religious -- from the tribal medicine man in the African bush to the one in the gigantic temple (hospital) in a Western metropolis. God could not instruct His people to visit pagans for medical care, because they were as likely to get incantations to Satan or his demons or other manifestations of the occult (for example, Eastern religious practices that are now entering medical care in the West), as any other form of treatment.

Satan can cause death and disease (see Job 1:6-2:8). Demons can cause physical or psychological manifestations (see Matthew 17:14-23 and Luke 8:26-31). Jesus' instructions to His disciples when He sent them out included driving out demons (see Matthew 10:8).

If Satan and his henchmen can cause disease, is it not also logical that they can *cure* disease, if by no means other than the withdrawal of the disease-causing influence? The Pharisees were aware of this relationship. On that basis, they thought that Jesus' ability to drive out demons was His authority by the "prince of demons" (see Matthew 9:34).

"Well," you say, "That was in Jesus' day. Western physi-

cians do not approach healing in this manner." You are partially correct. On the one hand, modern medicine is structured on
the Biblical worldview of an orderly, predictable universe of
cause-and-effect. That worldview is the basis of all scientific
advances. On the other hand, Western medicine has become
consciously atheistic over the past twenty-five years.

Thus, today, we are seeing physicians experimenting with
and using practices from Eastern religions and cultures. *If for
no other reason, we ought to be suspicious of modern medicine,
because its tremendous growth has occurred simultaneously
with the increasing godlessness of our culture.*

Gary North, in his book *Unholy Spirits*, presents extensive
documentation on several occult healers.[6] By these descriptions it is clear that their healing is real and that it includes
occult visitations and practices.

When God "breathed out" His Word through His authors,
He had to give instruction for every age and culture. To have
given explicit or implicit instruction for His people to seek the
care of physicians, He would have been directing them in most
cultures to His enemies and their fiendish works. He could not
even direct them to physicians who were Christians, because
they were often unable to discern what was Biblical and what
was not.

Yet, we are not so easily rid of medical care. I have not
presented the whole picture. *God's instructions do include the
use of modern medicine, but with considerable discernment.*
There are Biblical principles that we can derive for our health
and healing.

The Biblical Approach

First, *Christians should see only Christian physicians for
their medical care.* This principle should be obvious from my
Introduction and from Chapter 1. If health and the practice of
medicine are inherently religious, then the patient and the
physician should have the same beliefs. Many Christians are
on psychotropic (mood- or mind-altering) drugs when their
thinking and behavior ought to have been changed. Many have
been treated for sexually transmitted diseases without the pa-

tient's church dealing with the problem of adultery or even the spouse's being informed! Christians are given extensive workups that may or may not reveal disease, when they really need to be told that they are working too hard (often "for God"), and getting too little rest.

A significant aspect of this relationship is the availability of Biblical counseling for patients. The physician is trained primarily to treat physical diseases or discern whether or not one is present. Furthermore, his high overhead precludes the time necessary for him to counsel patients himself, and he may not even have spiritual gifts compatible with counseling (for example, exhortation, teaching and wisdom). Such counseling should be available, however. Ideally, it should be available through the patient's church, but at least it should be available locally.[7]

In fact, a Christian physician should not plan to set up a practice in an area where such counseling is not available, unless he plans to do it himself or bring someone into the community to do it. Physicians know the common presentation of psychological (that is, spiritual) problems in their offices. In the last chapter, we explored the interactions of the soul and spirit. Their unity will not allow for the effective treatment of the body without attention to the spirit, and it is a serious oversight to think that medicine can be practiced without attention to the spirit.

Admittedly, there are practical limitations. Physicians who are Christians and have the necessary discernment to practice such a distinctive type of medicine are not available to most Christians. And, a primary care physician often needs to consult specialists for problems in his patients, yet none who are Christians may be available. Thus, physicians and patients who are Christians will have to continue as best they can to find each other.

We must, however, know the Biblical ideal, if we are to move toward it. Christian physicians should have extensive training that includes as much *unlearning* of their formal medical training as new education. More importantly, the patient must know his responsibility under the Lordship of Jesus Christ to choose a discerning physician.

Many dilemmas in medical ethics would never occur, *if patients knew that their choice of a physician was the most important factor in the ethics of the treatment that they will receive.* Living wills or durable powers of attorney are not necessary where the physician knows both the limits of medicine and the limits of earthly life. Unnecessary and expensive tests and treatments will not be ordered by the physician who can discern the spiritual realities of the patient's condition. He will not withhold crucial information from his patients or lie to them. He will use prayer and anointing appropriately.

Until now, I have approached the physician-patient relationship from the standpoint of the patient. However, what should Christian physicians require of their patients in the area of beliefs held in common? Should they only work *on* patients, i.e., emergency treatment of the comatose or otherwise incompetent patient? Is not medicine working *with* patients? To what extent can the physician be *with* an unbeliever who, as it were, presents his *body* a living sacrifice to the physician, but who holds his *spirit* aloof, insisting on "nonjudgmental" therapy, i.e., therapy which by its body/spirit separation immediately disagrees with the Christian physicians beliefs?

And on and on. This whole book speaks of these issues. Modern medicine, as a reflection of modern society, has departed from God's Word. *Whenever this departure occurs, dilemmas are created that otherwise would never have arisen.* Medical ethics would be less complex within a Biblical worldview.

Shamefully, some Christians are only too glad to hide their sins under the unbiblical practices of medicine, just as they hide their sins in the church when they transfer their membership from a church that actively oversees and disciplines her members to a one that tolerates adultery, alcoholism, divorce, estrangement among members, and other openly sinful behaviors.

Health and the restoration from disease and injury are spiritual concerns and should be managed only within the Christian community. (We will explore the role of the Church in this endeavor in Chapter 12.)

Second, *the Christian is not limited to physicians or the traditional practice of medicine*. At first, this principle may seem contradictory. I have exposed the atheism and occultism of medicine. Am I directing us back to them? Not at all!

I am saying that physicians do not have a monopoly on the treatment of disease and disability. Even though they do have the most scientific approach, they also have their blind spots and their biases. We have already exposed their openness to immorality and the occult.

This position is not without problems. Impostors and quack healers are prevalent. As much discernment is needed when one goes outside the traditional practice of medicine as within it. (See "*The Health Robbers*" in Chapter 3.)

Generally, the following guidelines can be used to evaluate "alternative" therapies. 1) The most soundly based therapies are those of formally trained physicians and their traditional helpers: nurses, physical therapists, etc. (2) There should be little danger from the therapy. (3) An extensive training program has been developed by the "alternative" discipline and the therapist himself has had that training. (4) The cost should be reasonable. That is, the therapist is not employing a "get-rich-quick scheme" or taking advantage of sufferers with little means to pay. (5) The therapist should be a believer, as a Christian's physician should be a believer. (See Chapter 1.)

Third, *the church should be active in a healing ministry*. The anointing of James 5:14ff should to be practiced (see Chapter 5). Furthermore, elders must discern whether sick members of their congregation have an accompanying spiritual condition. (See Chapter 1.)

These three principles are the foundation for a Biblical practice of medicine. God never commanded His people to seek the services of a physician. While one cannot argue from silence that God intended for His people to avoid physicians, one can argue that His Word applies to all times and cannot be construed to apply in this instance only to the times when medicine was not "scientific." We are seeing that medicine continues to have serious deficiencies as a science and as a religion, giving further validation that medical care requires critical discernment in its application for Christians.

Refusal to Seek Physicians

There have been several cases in the past few years when parents, because of their beliefs, have not allowed their children to be treated by physicians. In some cases the children died. Do these parents or the state have the Biblical right to refuse treatments directed by physicians? The answer depends upon the medical problem and its treatment.

Generally, where the treatment is clearly effective, the patient and his family have the duty to accept it. For example, one family withheld care from their child who had pneumonia, and eventually the child died. Most pneumonias can be treated with antibiotics, so the parents were wrong to keep their child from a physician. This principle is that of the sanctity of the body (see I Corinthians 6:19).

Other principles, however, may bear on the situation. If the treatment is beyond the financial means of the family, and another legitimate source of payment is not available (for example, the church or voluntary organization), then the family would be right not to incur an unpayable debt. An exception to this principle might be temporary debt to allow the restoration of the breadwinner of a family who can then provide for his family and pay off the debt in less than seven years (see Deuteronomy 15).

If the treatment requires severe disfigurement or prolonged pain, then it may be refused. Such disfigurement was the first meaning of "extraordinary" measures, as far back as the 16th century.

If the treatment is questionably or marginally effective, then the patient really has the freedom to accept it or to reject it. When examined closely, many treatments fall into this category. For example, a common drug prescribed following heart attacks will benefit only 3 percent of the patients who take it (see Chapter 3), yet the medical literature clearly states that this drug is "effective."[8]

If the treatment has not been shown to be effective, it should be refused. For example, the cure rate for lung cancer is very poor and has not improved for the past 30 years. Thus, when physicians diagnose lung cancer, they should probably *not* attempt any curative treatment of it. An exception might be the testing of new drugs and techniques on a limited number of patient with lung cancer.

CHAPTER SUMMARY

1. The Bible gives no explicit instruction for a believer to seek the services of a physician.
2. All recorded healing in the Bible is miraculous. The Bible never mentions healing by a physician.
3. Even so, modern medicine should not be rejected entirely, but used with understanding and discernment.
4. Satan can cause disease and "miraculous" healing.
5. "Scientific" medicine does not have the worldview to prevent its use of occult and other religious practices.
6. Ideally, Christians should choose only Christians for their primary physicians. Christian physicians must also have certain spiritual requirements of their Christian patients.
7. No Christian physician ought to select a practice site where Biblical counseling is not available to his patients. If already in practice, he should seek to make it available or be trained to do it himself.[9]
8. Many dilemmas occur in medical ethics simply because the patient's physician is not a discerning Christian. The responsibility to choose such a physician falls to the patient and his family.
9. The Christian is not limited to traditional practitioners of medicine, if he is careful with the alternatives.
10. The Church should be more involved with health care.
11. The health practices of the Old Testament should be seriously considered for their application today.
12. Sometimes traditional medical care must be refused. Sometimes, it must be accepted. Sometimes, the right decision is unclear, and much time should be spent in prayer, searching the Scriptures, and in seeking Godly counsel.

Notes and References

1. Perhaps Asa was influenced to the point of defilement by idol worship because he did not remove the "high places" -- as commanded in Numbers 33:52 and Deuteronomy 33:29. King Saul had a similar failure in I Samuel 15, and God took his kingdom away as a consequence.

2. Rebecca A. Baillie and E. Eugene Baillie, "Biblical Leprosy as Compared to Present-Day Leprosy," *Southern Medical Journal* 75 (July 1982), pp. 855-857.

3. S. I. McMillen, *None of These Diseases* (Old Tappan, New Jersey: Fleming H. Revell Company), pp. 19-22.

4. Franklin E. Payne, Jr., *Biblical/Medical Ethics: The Christian and the Practice of Medicine* (Grand Rapids: Baker Book House, 1985), pp. 129-132.

5. *Ibid.*, pp. 106, 115.

6. Gary North, *Unholy Spirits: Occultism and New Age Humanisn* (Fort Worth: Dominion Press, 1986). This is the best book that I have read on the occult and its identity with New Age humanism. I highly recommend it!

7. All Christians should be able to admonish or counsel at some level (see Romans 15:14). There is, however, a place for pastors and others who have a thorough Biblical understanding to be formally trained in counseling and for whom counseling will be their primary activity or comprise a substantial part of their vocation. See Jay E. Adams, *Competent to Counsel*, (Phillipsburg, New Jersey: Presbyterian and Reformed Publishing Company, 1970), pp. 20-25, 41-43.

8. I have purposefully not named this drug so that patients who are on it will not begin to question their physician's wisdom. There are far too many variables in each patient that may or may not justify his being on a particular drug.

9. This factor is not meant to exclude other factors, especially those that would be necessary for the spiritual nurture of a physician's family, e.g., a Biblical church. Biblical counseling is so integral to the practice of medicine, however, that I have singled it out here.

CHAPTER 3

Physician, Heal Thyself !

"And he began to say to them, 'Today this Scripture is fulfilled in your hearing.' So all bore witness to Him, and marveled at the gracious words which pro- ceeded out of His mouth. And they said, 'Is this not Joseph's son?' And He said to them, 'You will surely say this proverb to Me, "Physician, heal yourself! Whatever we have heard done in Capernaum, do also here in Your country"'" (Luke 4:21-23).

Jesus was reading their minds! He knew what they really wanted -- firsthand evidence. They wanted Jesus to show them the "signs and wonders" that they had heard about elsewhere.

Do we not expect the same thing of modern medicine? Daily, we hear the news that some new medical breakthrough has occurred. In television commercials, we are told to see our doctor, if a particular remedy (being advertised) does not work.

Our belief in and expectations of modern medicine are great. To this end, "we the people" of the United States are approaching *one trillion dollars* spent and over 13 percent of the Gross National Product on medical care.

This belief in modern medicine is evident both at home and abroad. When a patient enters the physician's office or the hospital, he expects the firsthand reality of what he has heard. "Physician, you have healed others; heal me!"

I see the reality in my office. A patient comes in with symptoms of a "cold." "Doc, I began to feel bad and wanted to get treated before I get worse." In most cases, I explain that I cannot really relieve his symptoms any better than medicine he could have bought at the drugstore.

After this encounter, I charge him $35.00. By his reaction, it is obvious that he did not get what he came for. He wanted a cure. He wanted to avoid a further worsening of his illness. If I do not prescribe an antibiotic (in spite of my training and experience that it will not benefit a patient with his symptoms), he may become upset *and* may never return to see me again. I have not fulfilled either his expectations *or the expectations that are commonly touted for "modern medicine."*

This story could be told a hundred different ways. Minimally effective or ineffective treatment, a disappointed or angry patient, and a bill (often quite large) for medical services rendered is a common occurrence in medical practice today.

Yet, the hype continues. Patients hear it, and they come with great expectations of physicians. However, the "good news" of modern medicine is not so good. The physician is not able to heal himself -- or you! At least he is not able to do so very often.

Major Hurdle: The Non-Efficacy of Modern Medicine

Modern medicine in its entirety is detrimental to the health of modern man! Even if abortion is left out of the equation, this statement is true. Yet -- the United States is spending more than any other nation on earth *to make her people worse off than they would be without medical care!*

This obsessive dedication to "modern" medicine is the major hurdle to truly Biblical-ethical changes in modern medicine among God's people. You see, if modern medicine is truly a great boon for the health of modern man, then the expense may be justified. However, if my contention that modern medicine is detrimental to health is correct, then major changes must be demanded. *Who would want to continue to pay such huge sums for something that does the opposite of what is intended?* The "crisis" that calls for national health insurance would momentarily disappear!

This chapter can only be a brief introduction to this inefficacy, but enough resources and information will be presented to substantiate my position.

Empirical Uncertainties of Modern Medicine

My first book, *Biblical/Medical Ethics*, had the chapter,
"Empirical Uncertainties of Modern Medicine."[1] That chapter
was a lengthy review of the failure of the science of modern
medicine *with evidence from its own literature*! For example,
1) a strike by physicians in Los Angeles in 1976 caused a
decrease in the death rate for that period of time! 2) Studies of
medical research show that in many instances, it does not even
meet its own standards for "scientific significance." 3) Most
practices and prescriptions by physicians are without proven
benefit to patients. And -- many other examples taken from
more than 40 references.

A common first reaction to this evidence is that this data
dates from 1975-1985. However, that challenge will not hold
water. There is as much evidence (or more) today than during
that time. For example, 1) the war against cancer has been a
dismal failure.[2] 2) Thirty years of the treatment of prescriptions for ventricular arrhythmias has been shown to cause more
harm than benefit.[3] 3) A five-year study of intervention for
risk factors of atherosclerotic heart disease in men showed a
better outcome in the untreated group than the treated group![4]

I could go on and on *ad boredom*. I have files several
inches thick on such articles. These have been accumulated
over the years as I have perused and read the "medical literature" for other reasons. I have never even done a purposeful
search for such articles! The conclusions are the same: *The
very science of medicine cannot prove its own efficacy.*

A Look Back: False Credentials for Modern Medicine

The image of modern medicine received a great boost from
two classes of simultaneous events. One class was that of
social and economic change. The other was the disappearance
of certain diseases.

From the turn of the 20th century through the 1960s, extensive changes in the economic and cultural conditions took place
that made the United States a more healthy place to live.
Windows were screened. Outdoor toilets were replaced by

indoor plumbing, septic tanks, and sewage systems. Water treatment plants became a work of every city and county government. People became "more resilient, better educated, more resourceful, more trusting, and more supportive."[5]

Also, some diseases disappeared, sometimes because of these changes, and sometimes for unknown reasons. For example, rheumatic fever, a common cause of heart disease in children before the 1960s, virtually disappeared *before* antibiotics were widely available to treat the bacterial infection that causes rheumatic fever. Whooping cough, as a cause of death, disappeared *before* widespread immunization occurred. The spread of tuberculosis was halted *before* anti-tubercular drugs were available.

These two simultaneous events coincided with the rapid expansion of medical care and research. *Thus, scientific medicine received the credit for "conquering" disease and death.* While medicine may deserve some credit, the overwhelming evidence is that medicine had little effect compared to the socioeconomic conditions and simultaneous disappearance of infectious diseases.

Numerous reports and other studies fill *The Health of Nations* (see Note 5) in its 233 pages. Any reader with open-mindedness will read it and change his understanding of disease and death.

Quack or Physician? The Distinction Is Not Readily Apparent

The Health Robbers was published to protect people against "phonies, quacks and unscrupulous money-grubbers who prey on the insecure, the frightened, and the sick."[6] Chapters are written by a sterling list of more than 30 "expert" authors. A discerning reader, however, will soon realize that distinguishing the "real" physician from the "quack" is no easy matter.

The chapter on medical impostors reports cases in which people who have had no formal medical education have practiced medicine in various situations. One might expect that their ruse would have been quickly discovered, especially because modern medicine is so complex and "scientific." Quick exposure, however, is the exception rather than the rule.

These impostors are often quite successful. Testimonials to their effectiveness are legion. In fact, any prosecution of them is quite difficult when they are exposed as impostors, because their patients rally around them, giving firsthand evidence of their healing abilities!

A typical response to these cases is that the general public is medically ignorant and therefore easily taken in by these impostors. That response, however, does not match the facts of these cases. Physicians go through four years of medical school and several years of specialty training before entering practice. Yet, with little or no experience, these impostors function as physicians. Therefore, there must be a great deal about medical practice that is not complicated when *most* patients are helped by impostors! Indeed, the bandied figure is that *80 percent of all patients who enter a physician's office will get better - regardless of what the physicians does*. (Sometimes, they get well *in spite of* what the physician does!) And very likely, 80 percent is an underestimate!

That impostors can practice medicine and have most patients improve is additional evidence that medical outcomes are over-rated. Such cases also challenge current medical education, at least for the routine practice of medicine. If these impostors can function as physicians with little or no training, perhaps most of what the physician does can be carried out by someone lesser trained. Maybe that person can do it better, because both impostors and quacks (see other chapters in *The Health Robbers*) are known for their rapport with their patients.

Someone may counter, "Impostors are dangerous. They harm and kill people." Yes, they do, but not as frequently as might be expected. And -- physicians harm and kill people too! The impact of *The Health Robbers* may be an unintended one: the outcomes of both traditional physicians and "quacks" are altogether too similar! (Also, see page 42.)

Christians and Alternative Therapies

There are growing numbers of evangelical Christians who are changing to therapies and treatments other than traditional medicine. These changes are not all bad. In fact, I am "on record" as being favorable to such approaches (within some limiting parameters).[7] (Also, see page 42.) For sure, I have been quite critical of modern medicine both here and on many other occasions. However, Christians must use the same discernment for these alternative therapies as they do toward modern medicine.

The worst aspect of these changes is that the particular treatment or treatments become orthodoxy for those who endorse it. If you do not accept, even promote their method, they will have nothing to do with you. This fervency reveals that their belief in this treatment has exceeded their Biblical reasoning. The basis of fellowship with other Christians is always oneness in belief in the Bible and Jesus Christ (Ephesians 4:4-6), not something as particular as a method of healing.

Another danger in these changes is a belief that transcends natural reasoning. *By what criteria can any therapy be judged to be effective?* While modern medicine has its great faults, it has attempted a standard by which efficacy can be judged. Most alternative therapies seem to use testimonies of those who have been successfully treated. However, advocates of such therapies rarely, if ever, allow negative testimonials.

An attempt at scientific medicine has taught that 1) no therapy works in everyone, and 2) no therapy is without side effects. Now -- where are the negative reports about these therapies? At least, modern medicine has often published its failures and challenged its standard therapies. *On these bases, modern medicine seems to be more honest than Christians who promote these therapies!*

More needs to be said, but this book is not the place. Enough has been said here to state the challenge, *Caveat emptor* - "Let the buyer beware!" Perhaps, a review of the goals of medical care will shed light on the murkiness that exists among various "therapies."

The Goals of Medicine

"I don't think a medical student is ever told what his mission in life is. Certainly no one told me when I was a medical student what was expected of me as a lifetime goal in assuming the role of a physician."

C. Everett Koop, M.D., 1976[8]

Dr. Koop recognized a glaring and serious omission in modern medical education: the goals of medical care for physicians. That is, what should physicians set out to accomplish with their patients, *and what should patients expect their physicians to accomplish*? Unfortunately, physicians who are Christians have paid as little attention to this subject as non-Christians.

My first intention when I started to write on this subject was to develop a Biblical argument. On further reflection, however, the goals of medicine cannot rest directly upon Scripture, because there are no explicit instructions for either physicians or patients relative to medical care.[9] Thus, the goals of medicine are a derivative ethic.

Such goals could be supported with Scripture, e.g., to relieve suffering is clearly identifiable as a responsibility for all Christians. However, such support would be somewhat artificial when general instructions for all Christians are narrowed to the field of medicine. The important application, however, is that *the means used to achieve these "ends" (goals) must be consistent with and not violate any relevant Biblical principles*.

As a starting point, a physician's goals seem to be a two-step process: to diagnose and then, according to that diagnosis, to manage the patient. (I am purposefully avoiding "treat" for reasons to be explained below.) Obviously, management will be a more complex task because of the variety of options and possibilities that may or may not be available.

First, The Physician Is To Diagnose

To say that *a physician must first diagnose* what is wrong

with the patient who comes to him seems to say the obvious. This goal must simply be accepted as an axiom. No one can solve another's problem, whether medical or not, without first having some explanation for the cause of the problem. For example, when a patient with pneumonia caused by a bacteria called *Pneumococcus pneumoniae* reports to me that he has chest pain, I may diagnose only that he has severe pain. Consistent with this "diagnosis," I can give him a narcotic that will totally relieve the pain, but he may die from the infection. If, however, I proceed to diagnose the *Pneumococcus* as the bacterial cause, then penicillin will kill the bacteria and allow him to recover.

(I purposefully did not say, "the penicillin will heal him." The ministrations of a physician or any other "healer" always act in a specific way to allow the body to heal itself. In this case, there is nothing that the physician can do to actually rid the debris of the infection from the patient's lungs and replace diseased cells with healthy ones. So, in a real sense, "healers" are actually assistants to the complex defenses of the body.)

To diagnose is not as simple as it might appear at first glance. If a person with a form of arthritis goes to an Eastern acupuncturist, he will be treated to correct some imbalance of *yin* and *yang*. If he goes to a chiropractor (of the "old school"), his spine will be adjusted. If he goes to a medical doctor, he will be treated with an anti-inflammatory medication. (What is surprising is that all these treatments may "work" and the patient's symptoms be improved!)

Thus, one's fundamental understanding of normal and abnormal or health and disease determine one's diagnosis. As we have seen in the previous two chapters, a Christian has the spiritual dimension to consider in his diagnosis, as well as the physical dimension.

The first goal of the physician, then, is to diagnose.

Second, The Physician Is To Manage the Patient

The second goal of the physician is *to manage (assist) the patient*. I have avoided "treat" because, as we will see, the role of the physician is more comprehensive relative to patients.

First, under the broad approach of management, the physician is to heal. (I will use "heal" and "cure" as synonyms.)
The patient with some medical problem goes to his physician
who decides what treatment will heal the patient. *The difficulty
is that physicians are rarely able to heal.* We have just reviewed some of the problems that orthodox medicine has had
relative to its methodologies. In the large majority of instances,
physicians do something other than heal. These "something
else's" are the primary goal of my discourse here.

If a physician does not cure, then he may: 1) relieve suffering, 2) prognosticate (including reassure), 3) rehabilitate, 4)
prevent illness and injury, and 5) perform research.

Perhaps, *the most common role of the physician is to relieve
suffering.* This goal may be carried out in a variety of ways.
First, it overlaps with the goal to cure. Surely, the best way to
relieve suffering is to cure the patient of his illness or injury.
Second, a physician may relieve suffering simply by making the
diagnosis. Many people accept and learn to live with a condition if they know what is causing their suffering. Third, a
physician may alleviate pain directly or indirectly. He may
give an analgesic (a medication that is primarily given to lessen
or alleviate pain) and one that acts indirectly, but does not cure.
For example, aspirin decreases and may entirely alleviate the
pain of arthritis both by its analgesic and its anti-inflammatory
effect.

Fourth, a physician may relieve suffering through other
modalities. The blockage of an intestine by cancer may be
removed, while the cancer continues its malignant course. Pain
from cancer that has invaded the bone may be relieved by
radiation that shrinks the tumor, but does not kill it entirely.
Special wheelchairs, beds, and other appliances may be designed to make life more comfortable for patients. Modern
technology has surely provided great benefits in this area.

Fifth, the physician relieves suffering by his very presence.
I remember when I had infectious mononucleosis the month
before I was to enter medical school. I had run high fevers and
been in bed for several days. (I fully expected that I would
have to die before I could get better!) Just seeing the doctor
and knowing the diagnosis made me feel better and believe that

I would get well. Of course (as I know now), the doctor could not "cure" my illness, but *I had seen him.* In my mind (at that time), that in itself was almost as good as a "cure."

The role of the physician is to prognosticate. Medical education, including specialty training, teaches a physician something of the usual course of specific disease processes. His experience thereafter usually becomes an even better teacher. Obviously, however, this role is quite imprecise. Many people know a patient who had only a few months to live, yet lived for many years beyond the physician's prediction.

Prognostication, however, does have value. In general, diseases and injuries follow some, albeit variable, pattern. Again, knowing something about the unknown (the future course of the affliction) lessens anxiety and enables the patient and his family to prepare. The prognosis that death is imminent seems especially useful. Wills and living trusts can be set up, life-support measures that are or are not wanted can be discussed, and special efforts at reconciliation should be made with those whom the patient has unresolved conflicts (especially between husbands and wives).[10]

The role of the physician is to rehabilitate. Perhaps, modern medicine has made more progress here than in any other area. Intensive physical therapy, progressive re-education, and "space age" appliances go far beyond anything possible in the past. People who would have had to spend their lives in wheelchairs and/or be confined indoors now function at a much higher level and with little need for constant care.

The role of the physician is to prevent illness and injury, or further deterioration of health. As causative links between certain behaviors and accidents or disease are established, physicians are to warn people not to continue in those behaviors. While the majority of physicians' time should be spent managing acute illness and injury, they do have a unique perspective to observe such causative links. They can then pass on this information so that others may choose whether to continue in these detrimental behaviors or not.

The role of the physician is to perform research. If physicians did not build upon their predecessors, then medicine would not advance. Research, however, is more than that

performed in the laboratory or in clinical settings. Research
includes the physician in his everyday practice. He notes patterns of diseases and responses to medications and manipulative
procedures. He also notes *iatrogenic disease and injury*, as
many modalities of management cause their own unintended
effects, some quite severe and even deadly.

As noted above, the greatest distinction between "orthodox
medicine" and "alternative therapies" is the unwillingness of the
latter to do research. Without some systematic approach to
disease and injury, we actually know nothing. The courses of
diseases and the people who have them are too variable to make
conclusions based upon simple random testimonies. Under this
goal, then, these alternative approaches would be suspicious as
a valid means of medical treatment.

To Subscribe to an Objective Ethical Value

Non-Christians likely would not differ with the above
goals, although Christians and non-Christians might differ on
the emphasis given to each or allocation of resources for each.
It is the means to these goals that divides the Christian from the
non-Christian. Thus, the final goal for physicians in their care
of patients should be *to commit themselves to a stated standard
of objective value.*

Why is this goal necessary? First, the above goals are quite
general, and the means to their end can be quite varied. For
example, a physician may interpret an abortion as "relieving the
suffering" of a woman with an inconvenient pregnancy. For
the Biblical Christian, however, "Thou shalt not kill" (Exodus
20:13) proscribes that means. The same would be true of
euthanasia to "relieve the suffering" of a severely ill patient.
While the goal is acceptable, the means is not.

God says, "Thou shalt not commit adultery" (Exodus
20:14). Thus, the counsel and practices of Christians are not to
encourage or assist fornication[11] in any way. "Honor thy
father and thy mother" (Exodus 20:12) means that minor children must not be treated without parental permission (except in
an emergency).

Why should this goal be objective? Again, choices or

means (especially by fallen men and women) are too diverse to be left to individual (subjective) choice. While an objective standard cannot prevent wrong (unbiblical) practices, it will serve to restrict choices. For example, the Hippocratic Oath is an objective standard. If physicians subscribed to it, we would not have abortions today, as it states, "I will not give to a woman a pessary to cause abortion." The problem, then, is to call physicians to an objective standard and the Christian to the Biblical standard.

What must be realized is that we may agree with non-Christians on most of our goals, but we are strictly limited on the means to those goals. In fact, the failure of modern medicine to subscribe to an objective standard is causing an increasing difficulty for the Christian to practice medicine without offending his peers or even violating the laws of the state. It also allows the pursuit of virtually any means to achieve these goals.

Preservation of Life As a Goal

The goal of medical care is not to preserve life. Perhaps, more confusion exists today among Christians and non-Christians on what is or is not a goal of medicine than the above goals that I have already stated. "Heroic measures" are commonplace in virtually every hospital and nursing home where severely ill patients are simply "kept alive," with no reasonable hope of improvement in their condition.

That preservation of life cannot be a goal for medicine is simply proved by the fact that *all patients eventually die.* To strive toward a goal that is ultimately doomed to failure hardly seems consistent with any rational or reasonable argument. Yet, that goal seems to be assumed by physicians. Early in their training, medical students experience the breast-beating that goes on when a patient dies. "If only I (we) had done *this*, the patient would still be alive." This thinking is rarely carried to its logical extreme, that medically correct decisions can prevent all deaths. Stated in this way, the futility of that argument is apparent.

The Bible does not support the simple preservation of life

as a goal, either. Men and armies are called into battle to defend righteous causes (e.g., Judges 1:1-9; I Samuel 17). Paul went on missionary journeys that imperiled his life (II Corinthians 11:22-33). Modern missionaries answer similar calls, often to situations that endanger their health and their lives (as well as those of their families).

Further, the Commandment "not to kill" (the positive side of which is the value of human life) cannot be carried out *if an action violates another Commandment.* For example, I may not steal from others to provide for myself or my starving family (Proverbs 30:7-9). A woman may not commit adultery to preserve either her life or that of her husband or children (Exodus 20:14).

The sanctity of human life is a high value, but there are other values equally high, such as honesty and sexual fidelity. *There are even higher values, such as the worship of God and the righteous works to which He calls and directs us, such as missions.*

The Relief of Suffering As the Comprehensive Goal

Perhaps, all of the five other goals can be included under the relief of suffering. To diagnose is to relieve the anxiety associated with an unknown illness or injury. To prognosticate is to relieve the anxiety and uncertainty of the course and outcome of the illness or injury. To rehabilitate is to lessen pain, improve function, and give objective hope to patients. To prevent illness and injury is to obviate the need for medical care. To do research is to hope to improve all means to all the other goals.

Dr. Koop was correct. Goals for physicians are virtually ignored, except as they are implied by medical training and medical behavior. *It is past time for Christian physicians to clarify their goals and define the Biblical means to those goals.*

CHAPTER SUMMARY

1. The requirement of "Physician, heal thyself" has existed throughout history.

2. The major hurdle to a more rational approach to modern medicine is the recognition that its efficacy is unclear and that it often causes more harm than good.

3. Several examples of this lack of efficacy are given.

4. The efficacy of modern medicine rests primarily upon socioeconomic conditions and changes in disease patterns that had little or nothing to do with the actual practice of medicine.

5. Critical discernment between quacks and licensed healers may be quite difficult.

6. The movement among Christians toward alternative therapies is both good and bad. Most needed is some systematic approach to determine efficacy.

7. The first goal of medicine is to diagnose.

8. The second goal of medicine is to manage the patient in several ways: to heal (when possible), to relieve suffering, to prognosticate, to rehabilitate, to prevent illness and injury, and to perform research.

9. The third goal of medicine is to subscribe to some objective system of values and ethics.

10. The goal of medicine is not to preserve life, that is, to prevent death.

11. All goals of medicine may be included as the relief of suffering.

Notes and References

1. Payne, *Biblical/Medical Ethics*, pp. 33-49.

2. John C. Bailar III and Elaine M. Smith, "Progress Against Cancer?," *The New England Journal of Medicine*, 314 (May 8, 1986), pp. 1226-1232.

3. Louis K. Hine, *et al.*, "Meta-analysis of Empirical Long-term Antiarrhythmic Therapy After Myocardial Infarction," *The Journal of the American Medical Association*, 262 (December 1, 1989), pp. 3037-3040.

4. Timo E. Strandberg, *et al.*, "Long-term Mortality After 5-Year Multifactorial Primary Prevention of Cardiovascular Diseases in Middle-aged Men," *The Journal of the American Medical Association*, 266 (September 4, 1991), pp. 1225-1229.

5. Leonard A. Sagan, *The Health of Nations: True Causes of Sickness and Well-being* (New York: Basic Books, Inc., 1987). Quote is from the front dust cover.

6. Stephen Barrett, ed., *The Health Robbers* (Philadelphia: George F. Stickley Company, 1980), p. viii.

7. Payne, *Biblical/Medical Ethics*, p. 111.

8. C. Everett Koop, *The Right to Live, the Right to Die* (Wheaton, Illinois: Tyndale House Publishers, Inc., 1976).

9. Payne, *Biblical/Medical Ethics*, pp. 101-126.

10. Jay E. Adams, *Shepherding God's Flock* (Phillipsburg, New Jersey: Presbyterian and Reformed Publishing Company, 1974), pp. 128-156.

11. "Fornication refers to sexual sin of any and all sorts....(not just) sexual sin by unmarried persons (as it is used in American law)....Scripture writers used the word fornication (*porneia*) to describe *sexual sin in general*, and in the Bible it referred to cases of incest (I Cor. 5:1), homosexuality (Jude 7) and even adultery (Jeremiah 3:1, 2, 6, 8 ...) as fornication." Jay E. Adams, *Marriage, Divorce and Remarriage in the Bible* (Phillipsburg, New Jersey: Presbyterian and Reformed Publishing Company, 1980), pp. 53-55.

CHAPTER 4

Why Does Medical Care Cost So Much?

"Now a certain woman had a flow of blood for twelve years, and had suffered many things from many physicians. She had spent all that she had and was no better, but rather grew worse. When she heard about Jesus, she came behind Him in the crowd and touched His garment; for she said, 'If only I may touch His clothes, I shall be made well.' Immediately, the fountain of her blood was dried up, and she felt in her body that she was healed of the affliction" (Mark 5:25-29).

This woman's desperation came from the same physicians whom she had visited for help!

When she began to see them, she had only one problem: her hemorrhage. After "many things from many physicians," however, she had the additional problem that "she had spent all that she had."

Today, much the same scenario occurs. Patients have been to see "many physicians" and have spent a great deal of money. Yet, their condition has not improved and may have gotten worse. As we saw in the last chapter, they may have even "suffered" from these physicians. (One difference today is that much of the money spent is not the patient's, but a "third-party payer," a subject that will be dealt with later in this chapter.)

The cost of medical care has become one of the dominant concerns of American society and was reflected in the 1992 Presidential campaign. With Americans paying almost one trillion dollars and 13 percent of the Gross National Product for medical care, it is not only a social concern but a gigantic business and economic concern. The cost of medical care is

not only unaffordable by 37 million Americans (a bandied
number), its cost for individuals, families, and businesses is a
"big ticket" item. For example, the cost of medical provisions
to automobile workers contributes $1000 to the cost of every
new car that rolls off the assembly line.

Among Christians, no greater confusion about medicine
exists than the Biblical economics of medicine. There is always
difficulty separating "what is" from "what ought to be." Thus,
the existing structure of medical payment for the past 30 years
has inculcated the notion that its methods are "rights" and
"oughts."

Christians with the light of God's revelation should be able
to discern this issue. However, there are five major hurdles
that stand in the way to this discernment. One, the efficacy of
medicine, has been discussed in Chapter 3. That is, the
benefits of massive expenditures for medical care are in reality
quite small. The other hurdles are charity vs. government
provision of medical care, the right to medical care, the nature
of insurance, and the relationship of morality to health.

Charity vs. Government Provision of Medical Care

*The call for Christians to be charitable toward the less
fortunate is clear.* One illustration of God's judgment focuses
on acts of charity: food for the hungry, drink for the thirsty,
clothes for the naked, housing for the stranger, and visitation
for the sick and imprisoned (Matthew 25:31-46). The Apostle
James makes the searing statement that our faith (salvation) is
questionable if our charity is lacking (James 2:14-26). Charity
is to be extended even to those hated (Luke 10:25-37) and to
one's enemies (Matthew 5:43-48).

Perhaps, it is this strong and vividly illustrated call of God
that confuses Christians in the provision of medical care for the
"unfortunate." "If the government does not provide for them,
who will?," is the typical question when asked if such provision
is a proper role for the government. "The church obviously
will not and cannot provide the extent of medical coverage
needed for these people. Someone has to, and only the government has the resources (money)."

Two serious mistakes, however, have been made in such reasoning. First, government programs have been equated with charity. Note that the Bible passages identified above call for *individual* charity, not government programs. Other texts (e.g., I Timothy 5:3-16) call for charity from the Church. The reason is simple. *Charity, by definition, is voluntary. Payment of taxes (to give to the "unfortunate") is not voluntary.* Neither the individual nor the Church has any control over how the money is spent once taxes are paid.

Second, nowhere does the Bible give the state the role of charity. Gary DeMar has defined six Biblical roles for government, but charity or welfare is not one of them.[1] One might offer an "argument from silence." That is, whatever the Bible does not explicitly or implicitly prohibit is permissible. Since the role of government to provide welfare is not prohibited by the Bible, this role is permissible.

The defeat of this argument, however, is based in God's explicit assignment of charity to individuals and churches. *It is stretching the imagination that He would permit government funding of welfare by His silence when His explicit call is otherwise.* That method of design is comparable to the game, "Guess What I Am Thinking." More specifically, *revelation would not be necessary.* On this basis, mankind should be able to solve its own problems without any direction from God. Surely, no Biblical Christian would make that argument!

Thus, proponents who claim that God has given a role to the government as a charitable institution have no support either from the Bible or from any definition of charity as a voluntary and directed gift. As to who provides for the "medically needy," other principles must be covered before that question is answered.

The Right to Medical Care

John Warwick Montgomery has written a helpful book on the Biblical concepts of rights.[2] While he does not address the subject of medical care as a right, he does establish general principles that can be applied to medical care.

First, a demand for a right is always an appeal to authority for justice. It may be an informal appeal, as I appeal to my neighbor that his 100-decibel music has violated my right to tranquility. Or, it may be a formal or legal appeal to a government power (bureaucrat, politician, or judge) to enforce my right, as in a dispute over a property line with a neighbor.

In essence, then, a right is an appeal to an authority. Informally, it tries to invoke the conscience of another. *Formally or legally, it invokes the power of the government to force a person to behave according to some standard.*

For Christians, rights exist in two areas: the spiritual and the civil. In the spiritual, the ultimate power of the Church is excommunication (Matthew 18:15-20). That is, a person loses the fellowship of other Christians (I Corinthians 5:9-13) and may not partake of the Lord's Supper (I Corinthians 11:27-34). At a lesser level, Church leaders settle questions of rights between believers (I Corinthians 6:1-11). The Church has no Biblical sanction for the physical enforcement of rights.

In the civil realm, the ultimate power of government is death (the "sword," Romans 13:4). Lesser penalties are fines, restitution, and imprisonment.[3]

The most important point is that *the right to anything in the civil realm is ultimately backed by the power of the state with confiscation of life, liberty, or property.* Therefore, *the argument that medical care is a right is inevitably an argument for the government to use whatever force is necessary to protect and enforce that right!*

Many Christians have confused informal rights with legal rights. People in need have every right to appeal to the conscience of others to help them. As we have seen, one graphic illustration of Judgment Day involves individuals' responses to such appeals (Matthew 25:31-46). However, *the informal right to appeal is not the legal right to enforce.*

Consider the ultimate use of force in the issues of the "right to life" and the "right to medical care." Should the full force of the state (confiscation of property, limitation of freedom, and ultimately, death) be invoked to protect the right to life of the unborn (from criminal action)? The answer is a resounding "Yes!"

Now, should the full force of the state (confiscation of

property, limitation of freedom, and ultimately, death) be invoked to protect the right to medical care? The answer is a resounding "No!"

Think carefully on a purely pragmatic level. Is the right to medical care so great that others' rights are not only ignored, but seized and controlled that that right may be guaranteed? *Is the right to medical care greater than all the rights of others?* Again, "No!"

History supports this position against medical care as a right. *The current frenzy about the right to medical care is a new concept, even in secular minds.* The following was printed in the prestigious *New England Journal of Medicine* more than twenty years ago.

> "From man's primary right -- the right to his own life -- derive all others, including the rights to select and pursue his own values, and to dispose of those values, once gained, without coercion. The choice of the conditions under which a physician's services are rendered belongs to the physician as a consequence of his right to support his own life.
>
> "If medical care, which includes physician's services, is considered the right of the patient, that right should properly be protected by government law. Since the ultimate authority of all law is force of arms, the physician's professional judgment -- that is, his mind -- is controlled through threat of violence by the state. Force is the antithesis of mind, and man cannot survive qua man without the free use of his mind. Thus, since the concept of medical care as the right of the patient entails the use or threat of violence against physicians, that concept is anti-mind -- therefore, anti-life, and therefore, immoral."[4]

The Nature of (Medical) Insurance

The nature of insurance is that of an individual's being able to avoid financial disaster by pooling his risk with that of others. For example, the financial disaster of one's house burning down can be avoided by fire insurance. Financial provision for one's family in the event of the death of the breadwinner can be met by life insurance. Why not avoid the financial disaster of a major illness through medical insurance?

A major difference between medical insurance and other forms of insurance, however, is *an identifiable claim*. While the ashes of a house or a corpse are easily identified, medical problems are not. First, a medical problem must be diagnosed. For example, a patient has chest pain that has some possibility of its being caused by the heart. Now, note carefully. The physician of this patient cannot simply examine the heart in his office and determine the nature and extent of the problem as the insurance adjuster can identify the ashes or the corpse.

A "workup" ensues. Regardless of what is eventually diagnosed, this workup is costly. Thus, *one cost of medical insurance that may be excessive compared to other forms of insurance is the process of identification of the problem.*

Any number of diagnoses are possible. The problem may lie with the heart or it may involve the lungs, esophagus, stomach, or other organs. Once the diagnosis is made, the treatment may be a simple prescription, or it may require major surgery or complex medical treatment (such as radiation or chemotherapy).

So, *a second reason for the high cost of medical insurance is the complex direction that treatment may take.* A simple formula comparable to the number of houses that burn down in a geographic area is not possible with medical problems. So, a large number of possible directions must be included in the establishment of medical risk. This additional coverage is also quite costly.

Now, who documents and submits the claim for insurance payment? It is not the insurance adjuster, as in the case of fire or life insurance. The physician, who is not an employee of the insurance company, submits the claim. He chooses the "tests" needed for diagnosis, and he determines the treatment necessary for the identified problem. Thus, *a third unique cost of medical insurance is the loss of control of the insurance company in both the identification and treatment of the problem claimed.*

The patient himself determines a great deal of this process. He may decide that the physician's initial workup is not adequate and demand a more extensive one. He may go to a second physician, who will often go through the same workup again. As treatment is begun, the patient is often the sole arbiter of efficacy. Is his pain gone? Is he able to function in his work and at home? And -- how does he feel? Thus, the process and the outcome are governed to a great extent by the patient's subjective evaluation of himself.

This subjective dimension is a fourth unique cost of medical insurance. What the patient feels and is able to do can only be poorly quantified by objective criteria. He may claim continued pain, but physicians have no test for self-perception of pain. He may claim disability, when other patients with similar conditions function normally. Is he faking or truly incapacitated? Ferreting out subjective complaints and correlating them with objective findings is tricky at best.

Other variables that increase the costs of medical insurance are unexpected diagnoses that occur during a workup, iatrogenic[5] problems that occur, and unexpected complications of the disease process. By now, the complexity of medical insurance ought to be apparent. Factor in the documentation and paperwork for this process, and there are even more costs. Medical insurance is unique, and its inherent costs are many, many multiples of traditional forms of insurance.[6] Without quite specific limits of payment, its costs are really unlimited. Is it any wonder that medical costs are out of control?

Morality, Medical Care, and Caring

Morality correlates with good health. In the United States, emphasis and enforcement of rights and freedoms have greatly exceeded personal responsibility. This cultural and legal shift has contributed a great deal to the cost of medical care. There are few restrictions to applications for medical insurance other than "existing conditions" and use of tobacco products. Thus, a person may live the profligate life of his own choosing and be covered for the medical consequences of this lifestyle.

The disintegration of the family is one example. Numerous

studies confirm that married men and women are more healthy than singles (never married, divorced, and widowed).[7] Those married have fewer diseases, visits to physicians, hospitalizations, and "psychological" problems. And -- their children reflect similar characteristics for good health.

Thus, those who are moral (i.e., single and celibate or marry and stay married) have considerably fewer medical costs than the immoral. However, most insurance programs and no government programs have any criteria about being married or belonging to a family. Everyone's costs are "covered," while the reality is that the medical costs of the "immoral" are several multiples of those who are "moral." In this way, immorality is subsidized by both private and government third-party programs, and the costs of medical care are increased.

The extreme of total coverage for everyone is that designed for AIDS patients. State and federal governments have severely restricted the screening that private insurance companies may perform to detect people with AIDS or who are at risk for AIDS. Further, *government programs have been designed that reduce eligibility criteria and give added benefits to those with AIDS or at risk for AIDS*. Thus, moral citizens *both as private insurance purchasers and taxpayers* are required ("forced" because of the "rights" of some) to pay for the consequences of the immoral lifestyles that expose people to the AIDS virus.

In the previous section, the necessity of limits on medical coverage was demonstrated. One specific of that limit should be certain moral requirements. *Without moral limits, the medical bill for profligacy eventually becomes unpayable.* No society can afford to pay for the medical damage that immorality causes. We are seeing that reality in the United States today.

The *Christian Brotherhood Newsletter* is one example of the lower costs for moral people (i.e., Christians in this instance).[8] The "moral" (my word choice) criteria for membership are simply that those involved are "a Christian by Biblical principles, believe the Bible teaches you as a member of the Body of Christ to share other Christians' burdens, attend church regularly (three out of four weeks, weather and health permitting), totally abstain from alcohol, tobacco, illegal drugs, and..." (There follows some more details about specific requirements unique to their program.)

They also require a "waiting period" and exclusion of pre-existing conditions, similar to insurance companies. With these criteria, they are able to provide $100,000 coverage for a family for only $1000 a year (1992). Comparable coverage in secular insurance programs would be over $4000 a year! (I have not tried to cover every detail of their plan. Readers who are interested should write to the address in the footnote.)

Christians who believe that medical care should be provided regardless of the lifestyle of the recipient have failed to consider that God has placed restrictions on charity in specific situations. The Apostle Paul instructed the Thessalonians, *"If anyone will not work, neither shall he eat" (II Thessalonians 3:10)*. It does not take much wisdom to conclude that the person who is not allowed to eat will die of starvation within a few weeks. This harsh consequence is considerably less than a restriction placed on lifestyle to be eligible for medical care.

Timothy was instructed not to give *carte blanche* to widows, but to impose certain criteria that they had to meet before the church was to provide for them (I Timothy 5:3-16). One criterion corresponds to what has already been said here. "Younger widows" are refused, with the clear implication that they are to remarry (v. 11). Oh, such an odious restriction to "modern" individuality! But, nevertheless, this restriction is placed upon a woman following a great crisis, the death of her husband.

These texts and others clearly indicate that even charity is not distributed within or without the church without moral (Biblical) considerations. It is consistent, then, to expect that medical care as a form of charity ought to have restrictions as well. If a person lives an openly immoral lifestyle (i.e., "does not work"), neither shall he be eligible for charity in the form of medical care ("neither shall he eat").

Medical Inflation: Biblical Values and the Current System

Because man's resources are limited, he is forced to make choices about the property that he buys (house, cars, furniture, appliances, recreational "toys," etc.). It has been said that a man's checkbook reveals where his heart is. This saying is reflected in Jesus' words, "Where your treasure is, there your heart will be also" (Matthew 6:21). *As an objective measure of man's desires (heart), a man chooses from his limited resources.* The Christian, of course, should choose in a manner consistent with other Biblical values. These include physical provisions for one's family (I Timothy 5:8), the needs of other Christians (II Corinthians 8:1-24), and the support of missionaries (Philippians 4:14-16) and spiritual leaders (I Timothy 5:18).

Medical care is one choice among these objective values. The "right" to medical care has caused an attempt to provide full medical coverage for everyone. The glamour of modern techniques and medicine is so appealing that most people are willing to pay considerably more to have the "latest and best." In less than two decades, however, it has become apparent that *this cost is far greater than was originally expected.* In fact, this cost under the current system exceeded the ability of individuals, businesses, and even the government to pay.

This cost has several explanations. Some have already been discussed earlier in this chapter. Two more should be mentioned. Huge amounts of money have been poured into medical care and research to produce technology that is increasingly complex and expensive. Much of this money came from "deficit-financing." That is, the federal government spent money that it did not have.

Such financing was doubly inflationary to medical costs. First, it created technologies and treatments that would not have otherwise been available. Second, deficit-financing is always inflationary, causing the prices of goods and services to increase beyond what they would otherwise have been. Thus, in both percent and total spending, medical care and research has been one of the largest expenditures by both the government and the private sector. As a result, medical costs have consistently had the highest rate of inflation of all items for the past two decades.

Conclusion

The medical system in the United States (and to a lesser extent in many other countries) is built upon several fallacies that have been discussed in this chapter and listed below. *The recognition of these fallacies is prerequisite to a Biblical approach to medical care.* The current system is in shambles. Where churches and individual Christians have followed these same fallacies, they, too, have found medical care unaffordable. Fortunately, an occasional example, such as the *Christian Brotherhood Newsletter*, has shown us the Biblical possibilities.

The great enigma is why most people are willing to spend such exorbitant funds for results that are at best only minimally effective (Chapter 3). From a spiritual perspective, the far greater cost is a failure to obey God and His Word.

CHAPTER SUMMARY

1. The cost of medical care is one of the major issues of the 1990s.
2. There are five major hurdles that prevent Christians from exercising Biblical discernment in medical care.
3. The first is the lack of efficacy of the huge expenditures for medical care (Chapter 3).
4. The second is that government provision of medical care is an erroneous concept of charity.
5. The third is the newly conceived notion of medical care as a right.
6. The fourth is that principles of traditional insurance cannot be applied to medical insurance.
7. The fifth is that health is inseparable from morality. The costs of medical care without moral limitations are limitless.
8. The *Christian Brotherhood Newsletter* is one example of a Biblical approach to payment for medical care.
9. A distinction must be made between caring and medical care. Caring is possible without full benefits of medical care.

10. Present costs of medical care are a result of excessive and
inflationary spending by the federal government.

Notes and References

1. Gary DeMar, *Ruler of the Nations: Biblical Principles for Government*
(Ft. Worth, Texas: Dominion Press, 1987), pp. 76-81.

2. John Warwick Montgomery, *Human Rights and Human Dignity* (Grand
Rapids: Zondervan, 1986).

3. This statement is not an endorsement of the current penal system in the
United States.   However, a Biblical approach to civil punishment is beyond
our concern here. I have only pointed out what penalties are imposed today.

4. Robert M. Sade, "Medical Care As a Right: A Refutation," *The New
England Journal of Medicine*, 285 (December 2, 1971), pp. 1288-1292.

5. "Iatrogenic" means "physician-induced." That is, the patient is harmed
in some untoward way by the diagnostic method or treatment imposed. There
is good evidence that the incidence of these iatrogenic problems is increasing
and therefore adds to the cost of medical care.

6. These characteristics of medical claims make up a large part of liability
costs, as well. Thus, the costs of medical care extend far beyond their direct
costs.

7. Bryce J. Christensen, "Critically Ill: The Family and Health Care,"
The Family in America 6 (May 1992), pp. 1-8. Published by the Rockford
Institute, P. O. Box 416, Mount Morris, IL 61054.

8. *Christian Brotherhood Newsletter* is not an insurance program. It
simply publishes a list of the medical costs of subscribers in its monthly
newsletter, and payment is made directly from subscriber to subscriber. In
this way, it has avoided the state regulations that apply to insurance programs.
For more information, write Christian Brotherhood Newsletter, P. O. Box
832, Barberton, OH 44203, phone (216) 848-1511.

CHAPTER 5

The Trojan Horse of Christianity: Psychology and Psychiatry

"Then David arose and fled that day from before Saul, and went to Achish the king of Gath. And the servants of Achish said to him, 'Is this not David the king of the land? Did they not sing of him to one another in dances, saying:

"Saul has slain his thousands,
And David his ten thousands"?'

Now David took these words to heart, and was very much afraid of Achish the king of Gath. So he changed his behavior before them, feigned madness in their hands, scratched on the doors of the gate, and let his saliva fall down on his beard. Then Achish said to his servants, 'Look, you see the man is insane. Why have you brought him to me? Have I need of madmen, that you have brought this fellow to play the madman in my presence? Shall this fellow come into my house?' David therefore departed from there and escaped to the cave of Adullam" (I Samuel 21:10-22:1).

David demonstrated sanity in his insanity!

A paradox? Not at all. He avoided capture by simply resorting to insanity. (He did it well -- even letting saliva run down his beard!) By faking insanity, he showed his enemies that he was more sane (wise) than they were.

In fact, we might say that David was smarter than the psychotherapists* of our day, who believe virtually everything their patients (or "clients") say and excuse what they do. These "therapists" (with a few notable exceptions) typically free their patients from responsibility for their "mental illness" and from taking responsibility for their duties to others. These patients are made out to be victims of their parents or society who have "let them down" or have made conditions such that they cannot "cope."

*(Psychiatrists and psychologists function in virtually the same way, except psychiatrists are physicians [M.D.'s] who are able to prescribe medications and administer treatments such as electroconvulsive therapy [ECT]. Apart from these treatments, both can be considered together. Their philosophies rest upon similar foundations. I will use "psychotherapist" and "psycho-therapy" to denote both to avoid the repetitive use of both names.)

The situation is critical. Psychotherapists have a great deal of power in modern society. They have the legal power to confine virtually anyone to a psychiatric institution for a period of time *on their word alone*. They give "expert" testimony during criminal trials as to whether an act is a crime or an act of insanity. They have structured our prison systems for the rehabilitation of criminals (with the result that 60-80 percent become repeat offenders).

Psychotherapists gave considerable momentum to the abortion movement within the medical profession and in society, paving the way for the legalization of abortion (see below). They have given support to, if not initiated, all the social programs that deny man's personal and fiscal responsibility. In effect, *psychotherapists are the priests and the moralists of modern society.*

Worse, their understanding of man and their practices have infiltrated the evangelical church to the extent that they have a stranglehold on it. Psychotherapists comprise the pastoral departments of most major, otherwise conservative, seminaries. In effect, they teach God's shepherds how secular man has said that "sheep" should be tended. If we have major spiritual reconstruction in our country, I believe that this area will be the last to lose its influence.

King David has provided an example of the superficial nature of psychiatric diagnoses. If, however, he had attempted to escape in the same way today, he would have been locked up in a psychiatric institution, at least for a short time for observation! Let us explore some of the problems that have led to such a situation.

The Gray Area of Gray Matter

In earlier chapters, man was shown to have both a body and a soul. The most intimate relationship of these two components is that of the mind and the brain. The degree of influence that each has upon the other has been the subject of debate since man began to philosophize about himself. This debate continued into the last century until the concept (materialism) of man having a soul was virtually discarded. Now, man is considered to be no more than a complex collection of biochemicals and the evolutionary offspring of one-celled animals.

The Bible, however, is clear. Man has an immaterial component where he thinks. This entity is variously described as soul, spirit, heart and mind (Jeremiah 17:9-10; Matthew 22:37; I Thessalonians 5:23; Hebrews 4:12). In fact, true Christianity depends upon this concept. Jesus Christ was both God and man. He was both body (physical) and soul (spirit). *To depart from this teaching is to depart from the Christian faith.* Thus, anyone, whether he claims to be a Christian or not, who states that man is only a material being (that is, a collection of biochemicals) is speaking heresy. The concepts of body and soul are woven into the fabric that is Biblical Christianity.

What can be said, then, about the interaction of the brain (body) and the mind (spirit)? Some observations are apparent. When the brain is physically injured, the mind *is* affected. For example, a stroke that causes one area of the brain to die can cause a loss of memory, the capacity to talk, the recognition of family members and friends, the ability to do simple mathematics and awareness of one's own body. Head injuries from automobile or other accidents will cause similar problems.

Thus, physical damage to the brain does prevent the function of the mind in its relationship to the physical world. By definition, mind as spirit cannot be harmed by physical trauma, but it does seem that God has structured the mind-brain interface such that the function of the mind is limited by a functioning brain. Man is truly a unity of body and spirit.

The biochemistry of the brain is more complex. Certain chemicals clearly affect, and can even destroy, the brain. These include toxic industrial products and modern mind-altering street drugs. Altered physiology relative to cause and effect, however, is more difficult, if not impossible to determine. Two common examples are schizophrenia and depression. Both diagnoses have had hundreds of research projects conducted to determine what biochemicals may be involved in these problems. However, *the exact biochemical cause of these problems remains unclear*, in spite of this extensive research.

Three conclusions seem warranted. First, similar biochemical abnormalities are found in many, but not all, of these patients. Second, medicines that are given for these problems can change the behavior and functioning of these patients for the better. (Sometimes they are also made worse!) Third, if other organs of the body are subject to subtle disease processes, it is consistent that the brain would be subject to such changes. Thus, it seems quite possible *that biochemical deficiencies are present in some patients with "psychiatric" problems*.

However, even here, the "chicken-and-egg" relationship is not so clear. What is the cause and what is the effect? Did the biochemical disorder cause the behavioral problem, or did the behavioral problem cause the biochemical disorder? This dilemma remains unsolved. Certainly, thinking and behavior can change bodily functions.

Crudely put, modern psychiatric dogma says that behind every bent behavior lies a "bent" molecule (in the brain). It could easily be that behind every bent molecule lies a bent thought.

"Psychophysiologic diseases" are well-known among physicians. In these conditions, actual bodily changes are preceded by changes in thinking and behavior. For example, a continuing stressful environment can sometimes cause stomach ulcers.

Thus, repetitive abnormal behavior can cause these biochemical changes in the brain, rather than the abnormal behavior's being caused by the biochemical changes.

This gray area of cause-and-effect remains uncertain. Even the best (and most Biblical) counselors cannot always separate the patient's responsibility from the biochemical disorder. Likely, biochemicals do have a role in some of these problems. I cannot be dogmatic here. I would be less than honest to admit that this gray area concerning gray matter does not exist. As we shall see, however, this area is relatively unimportant to the role of psychotherapy in general and the distortions of Christians in these fields in particular.

The Big Umbrella

If psychotherapy were limited to this gray area where organic "mental illness" *might* exist, psychotherapy would have a legitimate role in medicine. However, the theories and practices of psychotherapists go far beyond these potential pathophysiologic problems. Psychotherapists "treat" problems of marriage and divorce, child behavior, phobias, stress, and situational conflicts. In general, they "treat" all problems that generate emotions, thinking and behavior, *even when there is no possibility of their having an organic cause.*

Psychotherapists make sweeping pronouncements about significant life issues. In Sweden, they have succeeded in making it a crime for parents to spank their children. In the United States, parents have been brought to trial and children removed from their homes because of spanking. Further, psychotherapists have created a massive social, political, and legal campaign to seek out child, parent, and spouse abuse. (While such abuse does exist, these efforts will further destroy family cohesion, and serious errors have resulted from overzealous officials.)

Prior to the *Roe v. Wade* decision that liberalized abortion in the United States, psychiatrists were quite willing to justify abortions for women for any vague notion of "emotional and mental stress." Rarely did any of these women have previous psychiatric problems. During the same period of time, young

men were often re-classified "4-F" (physically unqualified) for
the military draft solely for "psychiatric" reasons, again without
any prior record of such problems.

Today, most physicians look to psychiatrists to determine
what is right and wrong and to explain any unusual behavior.
Why else has homosexuality become an "alternate lifestyle,"
when it has almost always been considered aberrant behavior
and an abomination to the standard ethical code of a culture?
Why else is sexual promiscuity assisted by physicians with their
prescriptions for contraceptives to unmarried women and treatment of sexually transmitted diseases without ever mentioning
that such practices are bad for their health, as well as sinful and
immoral?

In essence, psychotherapists have destroyed all concepts of
self-responsibility and moral restraint. One's behavior is
always someone else's fault. Since that "someone else" is
usually a parent, psychotherapy has also destroyed family relationships. The slogan "Do your own thing" is no chance occurrence within this breakup of personal and family ties.

Psychotherapy has tried to destroy personal guilt before
God through such explanations. It has failed, however, because God has written His Law into the hearts of men (Romans
2:14-15). While the heart can become hardened (Proverbs
28:14 and John 12:40), these moral laws must be broken repeatedly for years to quiet the feeling of guilt. Nevertheless,
psychotherapists continue to try to remove guilt from the
human condition and especially from any responsibility to God.

Psychotherapists Who Are Christians

The word "Christian" is most accurately used as a noun and
not an adjective. Thus, there might be less confusion in the
area of psychotherapy if the noun were used more than the
adjective. Psychotherapists who are Christians are believed
(and they believe it themselves) to practice "Christian" psychotherapy. Christians flock to them for this reason. These
psychotherapists *almost without exception*, however, practice a
secular brand of psychotherapy with Bible verses and an occasional prayer mixed into their sessions with patients. It is

remarkable that *none* (to my knowledge) describe themselves as *Biblical* counselors, yet God has said, "...*The natural man does not receive the things of the Spirit of God, for they are foolishness to him; nor can he know them, because they are spiritually discerned" (I Corinthians 2:14).*

Certainly, all psychotherapists who are Christians should not be lumped together. They differ widely in their understanding and their approach to patients. In general, however, they show a superficial and often inaccurate understanding of even the basic doctrines of the Christian faith. (See "Suggested Reading.")

The most basic doctrine is that the Bible is the inerrant and authoritative Word of God. That is, God must be believed to have spoken in an objective and identifiable source before anything else about Him can be believed. Almost universally, however, psychotherapists speak of the "integration" of the Bible and psychiatric understanding of man. It is clear, and often explicitly stated, that this integration occurs between knowledge and truth that are equally valid.

God's own words, however, are clear in that His knowledge and man's knowledge are not equally valid.

> *"Then the Lord answered Job out of the whirlwind,*
>   *and said:*
> *'Who is this who darkens counsel*
> *By words without knowledge?*
> *Now prepare yourself like a man;*
> *I will question you, and you shall answer Me.*
>
> *'Where were you when I laid the foundations of the*
>   *earth?*
> *Tell Me, if you have understanding.*
> *Who determined its measurements?*
> *Surely you know!*
> *Or who stretched the line upon it?*
> *To what were its foundations fastened?*
> *Or who laid its cornerstone,*
> *When the morning stars sang together,*

And all the sons of God shouted for joy?'"(Job 38:1-7).
   "Do not be unequally yoked together with unbeliev-
ers. For what fellowship has righteousness with law-
lessness? And what communion has light with dark-
ness? And what accord has Christ with Belial? Or
what part has a believer with an unbeliever?" (II Corin-
thians 6:14-15).

   "Then Jesus said to those Jews who believed Him,
'If you abide in My word, you are My disciples indeed.
And you shall know the truth, and the truth shall make
you free'" (John 8:31-32).

Such verses with their logical inferences preclude even the
suggestion that the knowledge of secular psychologists and
psychiatrists is as valid as God's wisdom. Any attempt at
integration is seriously in error at best and heresy at worst.

Similarly, psychotherapists who are Christians say that the
Bible is not a textbook on psychotherapy. Here, they show
ignorance of definitions. The word "psychiatrist" comes from
two Greek roots: *psuché*, or "soul," and *iatros*, or "physician,"
literally, "a physician of the soul." (A "psychologist" would be
"a person who studies the soul.")

God says:

   "The heart is deceitful above all things,
   And desperately wicked;
   Who can know it?
   I, the Lord, search the heart,
   I test the mind" (Jeremiah 17:9-10).

   "For the word of God is living and powerful, and
sharper than any two-edged sword, piercing even to the
division of soul and spirit, and of joints and marrow,
and is a discerner of the thoughts and intents of the
heart. And there is no creature hidden from His sight,
but all things are naked and open to the eyes of Him to
whom we must give account" (Hebrews 4:12-13).

In light of these verses, psychotherapists' claims to understand the soul of man is ludicrous at best and pretends to do
what only God can do. At worst, *they pretend to be God!*

God's ordained institutions of the family and the church are
virtually ignored. Spouses are often counseled separately and
even counseled to separate and divorce, yet God has said that
they are to be "one flesh" (Genesis 2:23; Matthew 19:5). They
will give assurance of total confidentiality, when certain sins
are to be reported to the church and formal church discipline
applied (Matthew 18:15-20; I Corinthians 5:1-13). In fact, I
have never found any psychotherapist who has made reference
to the need for church discipline. And, it is uncommon in their
writings for them to make any reference to any role of the
church as necessary to the lives of their patients. They give no
consideration to formal ordination by any church, yet they
clearly function in a pastoral role, as "physicians of the soul."

Baker Encyclopedia of Psychology[1] is an example of such
distortion and avoidance of Biblical concepts. "Eminent Contributors to Psychology" include Freud, Adler, Maslow, Kin-
sey, Jung, Fromm and many others, but no theologians, Biblical characters, or God Himself are listed. This omission is a
clear statement that Biblical truth is not important to these
psychologists. Throughout the book, Biblical themes are
misrepresented, if they are mentioned at all. Examples are
abortion and sexual morality. "Love" is presented without ever
mentioning Jesus Christ, the ultimate Example of love. (Evidently, they believe that God is neither truth nor love!) A few
contributors reference the Bible, but they are a very minor
exception to the overall thrust of the book.

What Christians Who Are Psychotherapists Should Believe

I realize that many Christians find themselves in a career of
psychology or psychiatry. Further, Biblical counseling is not
yet widely available. Can any of these professionals continue
their practices without violating Biblical principles?

As I have discussed, there is a gray area where much work
needs to be done to understand Biblical responsibility in the
face of definable (now and future) organic brain disease.

However, there are certain fundamentals of the Christian faith that cannot be compromised under the guise of psychotherapy. Thus, the following criteria are meant to challenge those with careers in this field. Any disagreement must come on Biblical grounds, or the challenger is on "sinking sand."

Beliefs for Christians in Psychotherapy

1. Evangelism must be the highest priority when counseling an unbeliever. Salvation is what every person needs before he will desire right behavior and be able to live it.[2]

2. If a counselee chooses not to accept Christ, then he must be informed that he has rejected the ultimate answer to his problems and that anything else is, by comparison, worthless (Philippians 3:7-8). Counseling may continue if the counselee is still willing, since the possibility of helping him temporarily may allow the opportunity for evangelism to be pursued at a later session.

3. Counseling should never compromise an explicit or clearly implicit Biblical principle.

4. If the counselee is a Christian and Biblical counseling is available at his church, counselors must refer the him there.[3] Ideally, all counseling for Christians should have the oversight of the church.

5. A counselor should have read and essentially agree with *Competent to Counsel* because of its analysis of the place and content of Biblical counseling.[4]

6. A commitment to the Bible as the inerrant, infallible, and sufficient Word of God is an absolute requirement for the psychotherapist.

7. The real work of the Holy Spirit in Biblical counseling must be acknowledged.[5]

8. A Christian who plans to enter a counseling career should have thorough, formal, theological education rather than secular training. Counseling should then be done only under the authority of a church -- preferably as a pastor or an elder.

The argument is sometimes posed that the various fields of psychotherapy present opportunities for evangelism. However, more opportunities would be available by increasing the number of Biblical counselors. An additional benefit of an increased number of Biblical counselors would be their availability to those Christians who need Biblical answers to their problems. The Church of Jesus Christ must begin to demonstrate the reality that Christ and His Word provide solid answers to life's problems *far* beyond the possibilities a secular approach offers.

"All Truth Is God's Truth"

"All truth is God's truth" is the banner for psychotherapists who are Christians. The statement is intended to mean that truth from wherever it is derived is true. Now, certainly no Christian with a basic understanding of God would disagree with the statement itself. If a notion is true, then certainly it is God's truth. These psychotherapists, however, rarely, if ever, develop the philosophical basis (epistemology) that is necessary to their proposition. They fail to answer the question, "How does one know what is true and what is not?"

Psychotherapy has hundreds of approaches to the problems that it sees as its domain. Mostly, these involve a few basic approaches that are modified at will by individual "therapists." Christians in this area usually identify more closely with one form or another of these approaches. *Strangely, however, each one considers his approach to be true!* Yet, obviously, these different approaches cannot all be true. In fact, only one can be true, yet I have never seen a detailed argument by any one of them to prove his approach and disprove all other approaches. "All truth is God's truth" is a flowery phrase that is empty of content Biblically and philosophically. It also fails on its own supposed "science."

A Scientific Analysis[6]

Comprehensive studies of psychotherapy clearly show its failure to achieve its claims. Dr. Morris Parloff of the National Institutes of Health undertook a review of several hundred papers and studies on psychotherapy.[7] First, he found that psychotherapy is not a profession, but a varied and sometimes ill-defined set of practices engaged in by members of a number of different professions. In short, there is little agreement regarding what is to be included within the perimeter of psychotherapy and, more important, little consensus about what is to be excluded from its progressively elasticized boundaries. It seems that whatever anyone wants to call "psychotherapy" qualifies. There is no "standard" by which to decide what is and is not legitimate.

From another viewpoint, the failure of psychotherapy as a science is noted.

> "Modern psychotherapy antedates modern physics, biochemistry, molecular biology, behavioral genetics, and many other highly developed disciplines. We can no longer excuse the lack of hard clinical and scientific data either by the newness of the field or by the complexity of its problems."[8]

On the one hand, Dr. Parloff concludes that "the effects of psychotherapy can now be judged to be not merely modest but demonstrably great." This conclusion is based upon treatment outcomes in 475 studies that used 78 different forms of psychotherapy. On the other hand, he notes the "puzzling news" that effectiveness is quite limited. I have summarized his observations.

1. No clinically significant differences among the 78 varieties of psychotherapy were found. That is, any one was as good as another, even though each theory and practice was different from the others.

2. Fifty percent of the treatment effect is lost two years after the completion of therapy. Longer-term studies have not been done.

3. The more females in the study group, the better the results.

4. Patients did better when their therapists were similar in ethnic group, age, and social and educational status.

5. Patients who were chosen or who volunteered showed greater effects than those selected at random. This method is a violation of the scientific process itself.

6. Objective criteria, work adjustment, school adjustment, personality traits, and physiological reactions were less demonstrable of therapeutic effects than subjective criteria, global adjustment, self-esteem, personal development and experiences of fear and anxiety.

7. Comparisons across professions and schools showed no characteristic differences in the effectiveness of treatment.

8. There is little relationship between length of treatment and degree of effectiveness.

9. There is little evidence that the level of experience of the psychotherapist is related to effectiveness.

10. A careful analysis of nearly 500 outcome research studies still does not provide data adequate to answer the question of what kinds of therapy are most useful for what kinds of patients and problems.

11. Placebo effects account for about half the effects which were obtained by "recognized" therapies. That is, patients improved regardless of what was done or not done.

It is clear that problems continue with any "scientific" analysis of psychotherapy *by its own studies*. When Biblical criteria are considered, all such studies must be negated, because none are carried out with the intended purpose to glorify God (I Corinthians 10:31). *That many professing Christians who function as psychotherapists can be deceived in spite of overwhelming scientific and Biblical evidence to the contrary is strange.* Of course, Satan is described as an "angel of light" and his followers as "ministers of light" (II Corinthians 11:13-15).

Whom Should Christians Seek for Counseling?

Whom should a Christian with problems seek for help? First, he should see his pastor or other church leader who counsels *under* the authority of the church. Beyond the governing leadership of the church, the most knowledgeable and experienced Christian should be sought. Once someone looks for counsel beyond the church, he should not assume that a professional psychotherapist who is a Christian will give him the most Biblical counsel.

In some rare instances, medication or hospitalization may be necessary, but both the counselor and the counselee should be certain that all spiritual resources have already been tried and specifically identifiable physical causes have been investigated. Even if one or both these options become necessary, the pastor, elder, or someone else (as described above) must remain involved to prevent any compromise of clear Biblical principles.

I fear that even my mention of medication or hospitalization will encourage their use to the neglect of spiritual resources. Perhaps, it is a manifestation of our sinful natures that we will escape personal responsibility and confrontation under Christ's Lordship by any avenue left open. Both laymen and pastors must work diligently toward the full application of spiritual resources while remembering that a fallen world prevents a perfect understanding.

CHAPTER SUMMARY

1. Psychology and psychiatry have a stranglehold on the

Church.

2. Gray areas of understanding between thinking and behavior do exist, but are few compared to the extensive knowledge and domain claimed by psychotherapists.

3. Every area of thinking and behavior has been brought under the "big umbrella" of "mental illness."

4. Psychotherapists are the priests and moralists of modern culture.

5. Christians who are psychotherapists give greater credence to secular theories and practices than to the Word of God.

6. These Christians have a superficial understanding of basic Christian doctrines at best. Thus, they teach serious error at best and heresy at worst.

7. These Christians claim to have the power that only the Holy Spirit has -- "searching the heart" and discerning the "thoughts and intentions of the heart."

8. These Christians claim that "all truth is God's truth," without proof of their philosophical claim.

9. As science, psychotherapy fails by any scientific standard.

10. Christians should first seek counseling from their pastor and then others in leadership in their own church. Beyond the church, the ones most likely to give *Biblical counsel* should be sought.

Suggested Reading

Adams, Jay E. *Competent to Counsel*. Grand Rapids: Zondervan Publishing Company, 1970.

Adams, Jay E. *Christian Counselor's Manual*. Grand Rapids: Zondervan Publishing Company, 1973.

Bobgan, Martin and Deidre. *PsychoHeresy: The Psychological Seduction of Christianity*. Santa Barbara, California: Eastgate Publishers, 1987.

Bobgan, Martin and Deidre. *The Psychological Way/ The Spiritual Way*, Santa Barbara, California: Eastgate Publishers, 1979.

Vitz, Paul C. *Psychology As Religion: The Cult of Self-Worship*. Grand Rapids: William B. Eerdmans Publishing Company, 1977.

Notes and References

1. David G. Benner, ed., *Baker Encyclopedia of Psychology* (Grand Rapids: Baker Book House, 1985).

2. The basics of salvation are often erroneously discussed by psychotherapists. The seriousness of this fact should be apparent. If the basics of salvation cannot be clearly and succinctly stated, the psychotherapist cannot effectively communicate about the most important counsel for anyone-- that is, his eternal destiny.

3. Jay E. Adams, *Competent to Counsel* (Phillipsburg, New Jersey: Presbyterian and Reformed Publishing Company, 1970).

4. *Ibid.*

5. *Ibid.*, pp. 20-25.

6. This section is abbreviated from information in my book *Biblical/Medical Ethics*, pp. 165-168.

7. Morris B. Parloff, "Psychotherapy and Research: An Anaclitic Depression," *Psychiatry* 43 (November 1980), pp. 279-293.

8. *Ibid.*, p. 280.

CHAPTER 6

"It Is Appointed for Men to Die Once"

"Now it happened after these things that the son of the woman who owned the house became sick. And his sickness was so serious that there was no breath left in him. So she said to Elijah, 'What have I to do with you, O Man of God? Have you come to me to bring my sin to remembrance, and to kill my son?' And he said to her, 'Give me your son.' So he took him out of her arms and carried him to the upper room where he was staying, and laid him on his own bed. Then he cried out to the LORD and said, 'O LORD my God, have You also brought tragedy on the widow with whom I lodge, by killing her son?' And he stretched himself out on the child three times, and cried out to the LORD and said, 'O LORD my God, I pray, let this child's soul come back to him.' Then the LORD heard the voice of Elijah; and the soul of the child came back to him, and he revived. And Elijah took the child and brought him down from the upper room into the house, and gave him to his mother. And Elijah said, 'See, your son lives!' Then the woman said to Elijah, 'Now by this I know that you are a man of God, and that the word of the LORD in your mouth is the truth'" (I Kings 17:17-24).

Thus, Elijah performed the first successful resuscitation in recorded history! He was the pioneer of modern attempts to "bring people back from the dead."

At least, he is portrayed in this manner by some modern writers who discuss resuscitation. Elijah's actions do seem to indicate resuscitative efforts, as he "stretched himself out" (v. 21). Further, the passage does not say that the boy died, but that he stopped breathing. Of course, if someone stops breathing, he dies! In modern medicine, however, the distinction is made between cardiac (heart) and respiratory (breathing) resuscitation. In the latter, a person's heart still beats, so it is not necessary to do heart massage, if efforts are begun within a few minutes of the respiratory arrest.

Let's back up --- this maneuver was not a resuscitative effort. The boy was dead (his soul had departed - see later in this chapter). Further, the brain begins to die within a few minutes after respirations cease. Likely, some time passed between the time that he stopped breathing and Elijah carried him upstairs. More importantly, Elijah "cried out to the LORD" (v. 21), Who returned the boy's soul. The boy's revival was a miracle, not a medical maneuver.

In reality, a debate of this sort is irrelevant to the intent of the passage. God's purpose in this event was to prove to the widow that Elijah spoke God's words (v. 24). The passage, however, does bear on the claims and actions of modern medicine. It seems that, like Elijah and other Biblical characters, today's physicians can also "bring people back from the dead." Also, the organs of those who cannot be "saved" can be transplanted to continue the lives of others. Some even make the claim that life exists after death because of "out-of-body" experiences that some resuscitated patients have described after their ordeal. (See "After-Death Experiences" later in this chapter.)

As we will see, medical claims of "bringing patients back from the dead" and "saving" others by organ transplantation are greatly exaggerated. Worse, there are serious violations of Biblical morality in the macabre scene of open market and black market sale of body parts!

What Is Death?

Adam and Eve were instructed, *"Of every tree of the garden you may freely eat; but of the tree of the knowledge of good and evil you shall not eat, for in the day that you eat of it you shall surely die" (Genesis 2:16-17).* When they did not obey, they became subject to the curse that God had promised. But they did not die, that is, immediately in their physical existence. Most importantly, however, they died in their relationship with God. That is, they died spiritually, as instantly they experienced guilt and separation from Him (Genesis 3:7-8). They died in the ultimate sense, because health and life are literally communion with God, consisting of right standing with and obedience to Him (see Chapter 1). Physically, death became a slow process to which they would eventually succumb.[1]

Thus, a Biblical concept of death must associate sin as the cause and death as the effect. Paul makes this association explicit, "The sting of death is sin" (I Corinthians 15:56). Briefly, the Bible has four definitions of death: 1) physical death (Genesis 23:2, 50:26; John 8:53); 2) the second death or eternal punishment (Revelation 2:11, 20:14); 3) the life of every person after the Fall and before the regeneration of a believer (Ephesians 2:1); 4) a Christian's relationship to his way of life before he is regenerated (Romans 6:2, 6-7, 11, 13). Certainly, the primary focus of the practice of medicine is concerned (to a limited extent, as we will see later) with the prevention of physical death or the diseases that may cause physical death. The complete concept of death, however, must include all these Biblical "kinds" of death. In earlier chapters, we have seen that the most important dimension of health is spiritual health, not physical health or the treatment of disease.

Christians who are physicians must consciously connect sin and death, because this connection accounts for the overwhelming medical problems in the United States. That is, literally, "... The wages of sin is death" (Romans 6:23). In essence, then, evangelism and obedience to God's laws are necessary in any restoration toward a Biblical concept of health. Again, obedience must be emphasized, because to our shame, there is increasing evidence that the morality of evangelical Christians is little better than those who do not profess our beliefs. Thus, today's physician must be a priest (i.e., pastor) to Christians, as well as to non-Christians. Health cannot be maintained or restored without close attention to, and direction away from, personal sins.

A Time to Die: The Golden Rule

> *"To everything there is a season,*
> *A time for every purpose under heaven:*
>
> *A time to be born,*
> *And a time to die" (Ecclesiastes 3:1-2).*

Earlier in this century, pneumonia was called "the old man's friend." Today, we still sometimes say that dying in one's sleep or quietly at home is a "blessing." Both sayings reflect an understanding that death is inevitable and that the sufferings of old age can be difficult to bear for both the afflicted person and his family. This attitude is Biblical, if the proper balance of the following Biblical principles is maintained.

First, *the avoidance of suffering may never be a criterion by which death may be sought.* That is not to say that chronic illness, brain damage and terminal illness are not extremely difficult. In fact, these problems demonstrate graphically the ravaging, ugly nature of sin. Adam and Eve were made to live forever in their youthful vigor. Thus, any disease and disfigurement is directly or indirectly caused by sin.

(We have previously considered the balance to be maintained concerning the direct effect of personal sin vs. the general effect of sin on all mankind as descendants of Adam and Eve.)

In my mind, nursing homes graphically illustrate these tragic effects of sin on the human body and mind. Here, one encounters human beings with blank stares, contracted and distorted limbs, foul smells, rotting flesh, and copious and nauseating discharge of body fluids. These patients are maintained by various medications and modes of physical therapy. Almost all were once wonderfully youthful and vigorous.

In conversations with people and in a few surveys, a consistent desire (especially among the elderly) is not to be kept alive by "heroic" means when there is virtually no hope of recovery. Do you? I don't. Curiously, however, relatives and physicians fail to act on this common desire. "Everything" will be attempted for the other person, where it is not desired for oneself. A reason for this discrepancy may include a concern for "appearances." That is, one's level of caring is judged by how much is done for "Aunt Mary" or whomever. Another reason is the physicians' and nurses' belief that their role is to maintain life at all costs.

But the question for Christians is, "Is this desire Biblical?" Clearly, it is. The Golden Rule is central. "Do unto others as you would have them do unto you" (the common wording of Luke 6:31). By nature, those who are concerned with ethics (Biblical ethics is no exception) want a rule for every situation. Life in general, however, and severe illnesses in particular cannot always be fitted into neat, tidy rules. Although the problem among Christians has been too little Biblical application to medical ethics, errors can be made at the other extreme, as well. Whether we like it or not, some life situations force us to allow a degree of subjectivity. That is, the participants in a situation must be allowed some freedom *within Biblical principle* to choose a course of action. The Golden Rule allows this process of choosing.

A current debate rages among pro-life people whether water and food should be withheld in comatose and terminally ill patients. Each side makes a serious mistake that violates a Biblical principle. The advocates of the "do-everything" side (the majority of "pro-lifers" seem to take this position) rail about the horrors of dehydration and starvation. The advocates of the "don't-do-everything" side use suffering as a reason to discontinue treatment.   Let us consider the errors in these directives.

The "do-everything" side does not consider the horrors of the condition of these patients and the ineffectiveness of medical and nursing care to improve the patients' conditions, much less to restore them to some semblance of normality. Further, they do not consider that these patients will die of some problem that may be as gruesome, or worse, than dehydration and starvation. They seem to pretend that these patients can be effectively treated and that they will eventually die a quiet death.

I described a typical nursing home scene above. These conditions are the usual experience of severely ill patients who are "kept alive." Their "dying" may include the rigors of repeated resuscitations, overwhelming infections, pulmonary emboli (blood clots that travel to the lungs), strokes, amputations, tubes in various bodily orifices, and mild-to-severe reactions to medications. Surely these problems compare with the difficulties of dehydration and starvation and many are worse. The point here is that these patients face a severely difficult existence, *whatever is done*. To pretend that dehydration and starvation are somehow more gruesome than these other problems is to distort the inherent difficulty of severe disease and disability.

A criterion that may help in these situations is the degree to which a patient may be restored to his previous "healthy" state. (See "The Goals of Medicine" in Chapter 3.) Some diseases or injuries have a strong likelihood of recovery. Others have an equally strong likelihood of little or no recovery. Certainly, in the former conditions every effort should be made to ensure the patients' recovery. The latter conditions are those where we should apply the Golden Rule. Merely keeping a person "alive" does not seem to be a proper goal for medicine. As we have seen, dying and death are inevitable, and we should realize the point where all our medical resources are futile to restore the person to his former state of health.

A Biblical example is the reaction of David to the news of the death of the child born to Bathsheba (II Samuel 12:19-23). David had been pleading with utmost intensity for God to spare the child's life. His prayers could have continued even after the child's death, knowing that God was able to resurrect him, if He chose to do so. David, however, recognized a time after which prayer was no longer indicated. That is, he recognized a time for efforts at restoration of the child to cease. We ought also to recognize a time for our efforts to cease.

The "don't-do-everything" side does not consider the Biblical principle that suffering is a significant dimension of the process of sanctification.

"My son, do not despise the chastening of the Lord,
Nor be discouraged when you are rebuked by Him;
For whom the Lord loves He chastens,

And scourges every son whom he receives."

"If you endure chastening, God deals with you as with sons; for what son is there whom a father does not chasten? But if you are without chastening, of which all have become partakers, then you are illegitimate and not sons.... Now no chastening seems to be joyful for the present, but grievous; nevertheless, afterward it yields the peaceable fruit of righteousness to those who have been trained by it" (Hebrews 12:5-8, 11).

"My brethren, count it all joy when you fall into various trials, knowing that the testing of your faith produces patience. But let patience have its perfect work, that you may be perfect and complete, lacking nothing" (James 1:2-4).

Disease and disability are one aspect of this suffering for both the patient and his family. *To use suffering as the reason to hasten death by any means is to thwart one of God's clearly stated means of sanctification.* Realistically, these situations are wearying and severely test one's ability to think clearly. We must not underestimate their emotional impact.

Nevertheless, the more important focus here is that the trial is from God and that He is in control.

"No temptation (or trial) has overtaken you except such as is common to man; but God is faithful, who will not allow you to be tempted beyond what you are able, but with the temptation will also make the way of escape, that you may be able to bear it" (I Corinthians 10:13).

"And let us not grow weary while doing good, for in due season we shall reap if we do not lose heart" (Galatians 6:9).

The extreme application of those who seek death as a relief for suffering is euthanasia, usually by a lethal injection. The Biblical position stands in stark contrast to this approach. God says, "Thou shalt not kill." Secular ethicists says that a lethal injection in these situations is no different from withholding or withdrawing medical treatment. The Christian sees a difference as distinct as night and day. While the Golden Rule (and considerations that follow) may call us not to "do everything," we cannot kill in this manner.

Second, *Paul does not value continued physical life over death that brings "life" with Jesus Christ.*

> *"Therefore we are always confident, knowing that while we are at home in the body we are absent from the Lord. For we walk by faith, not by sight. We are confident, yes, well pleased rather to be absent from the body and to be present with the Lord" (II Corinthians 5:6-8).*

> *"For to me, to live is Christ, and to die is gain. But if I live on in the flesh, this will mean fruit from my labor; yet what I shall choose I cannot tell. For I am hard pressed between the two, having a desire to depart and be with Christ, which is far better" (Philippians 1:21-23).*

Paul's attitude contrasts with modern scenes in ICUs, organ transplantations, and resuscitative efforts. Paul considered himself "with Christ," whether in his physical body on earth or in Heaven. I seriously doubt that he would have chosen modern "heroic measures" to sustain his life beyond the point that he was able to serve Jesus Christ on earth.

Third, *economics is a limiting factor for continued life support.* Costs for life support, whether in the hospital or in a nursing home, are extremely high. Currently, the larger portion of these costs is paid by federal and state governments, either through taxes (involuntary redistribution) or deficit-financing (debt without the ability to repay). Thus, the Eighth Commandment is violated either way. To continue to pay for these "end-of-life costs" is to continue to accept the immoral methods of our government.

Further, any inheritance that a person may have can be *quickly* wiped out by medical treatment that is not covered by insurance or the government. Everyone must consider what he will leave his children (II Corinthians 12:14). Careful legal arrangements must be made to prevent this loss of inheritance, if that is the parents' desire. We have already seen that God does not require that we indulge in every available medical means of continued life support.

One final point needs to be made for clarity. Although I do not advocate the "do-everything" approach, efforts must *always* be made to keep patients comfortable and to minimize their suffering. Too often, those who are critical of the "don't-do-everything" approach accuse its advocates of being insensitive to the suffering of patients and even abandoning them. *What we advocate is a limitation of medical treatment for the reasons that we have presented, not a limitation of care.* Chapter 3 intended to decrease the "god" status of modern medicine. To suggest the restriction of medical care in carefully considered circumstances is not necessarily consistent with lesser care of the patient. Medical treatment may cause *more* suffering for patients, and the treatment itself may be ineffective or harmful.

Brain Death and Organ Transplantation

Modern technology has led to the concept of "brain death." As recently as 25 years ago, when the heart or respiration stopped, the person was declared dead, because nothing could be done. Now, the function of both heart and lungs can in many instances be sustained indefinitely with respirators and other support. Thus, patients are kept "alive" beyond the time when they would have died without these means. Since these patients hardly seem "alive," brain-death criteria were developed to allow physicians to end life support for some patients (and to allow for organ transplantation).

The formal definition of brain death is called the Uniform Determination of Death Act (UDDA).

"An individual who has sustained either (1) irre-

versible cessation of circulatory and respiratory func
tions, or (2) irreversible cessation of all functions of the
entire brain, including the brain stem, is dead. A
determination of death must be made in accordance
with accepted medical standards."

At first glance, these criteria seem to help us know when to
stop treatment. This conclusion, however, is wrong.

First, the criteria are not practical, because few patients
fulfill them. Most patients with brain damage have some
remaining brain function. In fact, most patients with severe
brain damage have considerable brain function *relative to these
standards*. (Relative to normal brain function, they have considerable loss). Thus, these criteria apply to a small percentage
of patients and still leave us the large majority of brain-
damaged patients without criteria upon which to continue or
terminate treatment. Further, all patients who fit these criteria
die within a few days or weeks *regardless* of what is done. It
seems that without some brain function, the medical complications are overwhelming.

Second, by Biblical criteria, these people are not dead. The
reasoning is quite simple. All human beings fit into one of two
categories relative to their life on earth. They are either alive
or dead. *Death occurs when the soul leaves the body* (Eccle-
siastes 3:21; James 2:26), as Adam become alive when God
breathed a "living soul" into him (Genesis 2:7). Life requires
the presence of the soul. Physical death occurs at the time that
the soul leaves the body. Thus, is the soul present in the
"brain-dead" person? Honestly, we don't know for certain.
The physical senses cannot detect spiritual reality. *"We walk
by faith and not by sight"* (II Corinthians 5:7).

The more important question, however, is, "What compelling reason do we have to say that the brain-dead person does
not have a soul?" Is a human being's life reducible to one organ
(the brain)? If we believe that man is a unity of all his parts,
then we cannot limit his being to his brain. Of course, many
evidences indicate that the soul has some special relationship to
the brain. Still, it is going too far to say that determination of
"life" is limited to the presence or absence of brain activity.

For example the embryo has no brain function, but he is most definitely alive. The brain-dead person is likewise alive.

I am not saying that brain death is not a reason to cease medical treatment. That statement should be apparent from the preceding section. In fact, I advocate the cessation of medical treatment for less than brain-death criteria. It may seem to be splitting hairs to say that the brain-dead person is alive, but it is vital for the embryo, and vital for the status of the brain-dead person. The following may make the importance of this position more clear.

Transplantation: What Organs May or May Not Be Removed?

It may be going too far to say that UDDA criteria came about to enable major organs to be taken from donors and transplanted into others. Nevertheless, these criteria are necessary to declare officially that a person is dead in order to remove his organs. This necessity exists because *the removal of major organs (heart, lungs, or both together) is in essence the cause of the patient's death.* If the person is already dead by UDDA, then the organs have not been removed from a living person, but a cadaver. (Note the contrast here - a living "brain-dead" person vs. the stiff, cold body that we associate with the word "cadaver.")

If one takes the position that brain-dead people still have their souls and are alive, then transplantation of their hearts or heart-lungs (lung transplants without the donor heart are not successful) is not morally permissible. In effect, the removal of their organs causes their deaths. They may have died shortly anyway from their injuries, but if the heart is removed, that operation becomes the cause of death (upon removal of life-support mechanisms). It is no longer the injuries that the person dies of, but the removal of his heart. Simply, *if the person is alive, we cannot do anything that will cause his death, or we violate the Sixth Commandment.* It does not matter that he will die anyway without life support. The same argument could be applied to any person in any situation, since everyone dies eventually.

Removal of the liver or kidneys is permissible, because

their removal does not cause immediate death. The toxins that would build up in the injured person's body from the absence of these organs would not accumulate sufficiently to cause the person's death for several hours or days. The patient would die of his injuries when life support is turned off, long before the absence of these organs would kill him. Corneas, skin, and bones can be taken shortly after death, so their transplantations would also be permissible.

Economics is also a major factor in the transplants of hearts, heart-lungs and livers. Who should pay? We have eliminated the government as a moral agent to pay for medical care (Chapter 4). Private insurance is a possibility, but an increase in the number of these procedures would cause premiums to skyrocket. Few families can afford the $100,000 and more that is necessary for these transplants. Thus, such transplants are virtually precluded by their cost. The few that might be afforded by wealthy families or charity would be impractical, because the success of such complex procedures is dependent upon a certain volume to develop and refine the skills and knowledge requisite to successful outcomes.

This cost prohibition seems to unify a Biblical prohibition against these transplants. Not only are they immoral by the Biblical criterion of death (a violation of the Sixth Commandment), they are unaffordable to most people except through immoral means (a violation of the Eighth Commandment). The commandments agree in their prohibition of major organ transplants.

"After-Death Experiences"

The Biblical criterion that we have established also precludes the possibility of "after-death experiences." Such accounts are reported by some people who have undergone resuscitation or critical injuries. They supposedly died and were resurrected. Some "experts" have even gone so far as to say that these experiences are evidence for life after death. Often, an encounter with a "white being," whom some have thought to be Jesus, is described.

If we believe that death occurs upon the departure of the

soul, then these people were never really dead. Only God is able to unite soul and body. Certainly, medical science is not able to do so! Further, "it is appointed for men to die *once*" (Hebrews 9:27, emphasis added). Except for the few exceptions of resurrections in the Bible, all other humans die only once. Thus, these phenomena, as dramatic and unexplained as they may be, cannot be after-death experiences. That similar experiences occur in life-threatening situations where injury does not actually occur also supports the contention that the phenomena are caused by something that does not require the actual death of the person.

Priorities for Families

Living wills. These are unbiblical because authority is transferred from the family to the state. Biblical authority resides within the family primarily and within the church secondarily. Husbands and wives, regardless of their age, should discuss with each other what they do or do not want to be done medically, if they should become seriously injured or ill. Elderly people who are widowed or single should talk with their most responsible children or other relatives.

Powers of attorney and wills. All husbands and wives should have durable power of attorney for each other, as well as a will. The former becomes necessary at any time that one spouse is unable to function legally. Biblically, these are not necessary, because God ordains the responsibility of one spouse for the other when one is unable to carry out his or her responsibilities.

Under our legal system, however, they are necessary for one spouse to act legally for the other. These ought to be drawn up immediately, because accidents and diseases can come unexpectedly, even in the young and healthy. Powers of attorney cover those situations in which death does not occur, but incapacitation does. Further, most states will not appoint an out-of-state resident to be appointed guardian of an incompetent person. They will, however, honor a power of attorney given to an out-of-state resident. Also, in many states the power of attorney for medical matters requires a separate document from the general power of attorney.

Wills direct the legal management of the dead person's estate. Everyone who has anything that he would like to direct to a particular person after his own death should have a will. Again, these should be drawn up immediately. Our efforts as Christians are to avoid the state's interference in our lives and property in all areas in which we still have freedom.

Choice of physician. Ultimately, physicians have to decide whether a situation is hopeless relative to physical recovery of a patient. It is the information that he provides that a family will use to make other decisions. Thus, the choice of a physician is extremely important in these situations. Some physicians do not give any options to the family! Of course, every potential situation cannot be discussed with your physician beforehand, but his general approach to these issues can be. Christians can hope that one day there will be a registry of Christian physicians who have been trained in the application of Biblical principles (see Chapter 11).

Insurance. It is impossible to prepare for all catastrophes that may occur. Insurance, however, is one method by which the risk can be shifted among a large group. Wise counseling is necessary in one's choice of policies for all types of insurance. We are most concerned here with health, disability and life insurance. The church has a particular interest in these, because it is the "backup" to provide the care that its members are unable to afford. (See Chapter 4.)

Loss of Control

The immoral authority given to medicine by the state often takes medical decisions out of the hands of the family. For example, one elderly man was comatose with a severe chronic illness. Both he and his wife were devout Christians. When she asked that all artificial measures of life support be terminated, she was denied the right to make that decision. Yet, she continues to be responsible for his medical bills!

The legal alternatives for similar situations is beyond the scope of this chapter and this book. Christians, however, must begin to reason together how to avoid this takeover by the state.

Not inconceivably, one's entire estate could be spent on medical care without his permission. Those in this situation will have to engage a lawyer to help them determine legal options. The presence of durable powers of attorney may preclude some problems in this situation, and perhaps other documents can be drawn up to prevent this confiscation by the state.

Reconciliation

Most relationships within families, even Christian families, carry excess "baggage." That is, there are numerous hurts, slights and other ongoing offenses that have not been reconciled. Although the necessity should be obvious, when a member of a family is dying, they face a last opportunity for such reconciliation. Without it, communication will continue to be difficult and incomplete during this time of great stress. If not resolved before the person dies, then guilt over these unreconciled areas can be difficult to overcome.

Of course, the patient may not be sufficiently conscious for such reconciliation to occur. That reason, however, is the only one that should preclude this important matter. Dr. Jay Adams has some specific directions for families and pastors to deal with this situation.[2]

CHAPTER SUMMARY

1. Death is inherently a spiritual concept, being caused by the sin of Adam and Eve.
2. There are four "kinds" of death in the Bible: physical death, regeneration (death to the "old man"), spiritual death before regeneration, and the second death (eternal punishment).
3. The avoidance of suffering is not a valid criterion upon which to seek death.
4. The Golden Rule is a reasonable guideline whether to continue or discontinue life support in severely ill patients and allows for the flexibility necessary to govern these complex situations.
5. Physical life can be (but should not be) wrongly elevated

above other Biblical principles

6. Economics is a major factor in "end-of-life" issues.
7. Patients should never be neglected, nor their suffering minimized, even though limited medical treatment may be limited.
8. The formal (UDDA) definition of brain death fails practically and Biblically.
9. The Biblical concept of death precludes the transplantation of heart, lungs, pancreas, stomach, and other unpaired essential organs.
10. Most major organ transplantations would be precluded on the basis of cost alone in a truly "free" market.
11. "After-death experiences" are misnomers. People who are truly dead do not come back to life.
12. Living wills are a wrong transference of family authority to the state.
13. Durable powers of attorney and wills are necessary legal documents, regardless of age or health status in today's medical-legal climate.
14. Life and health insurance are necessary to avoid financial hardships on families.
15. A family's choice of a physician may be the most important decision that they make concerning end-of-life issues.
16. Families are losing control over medical decisions for their members with the increasing intrusion of the state into health care.
17. Families must give particular attention to reconciliation with a dying member. Pastoral oversight is a necessity in these situations.

Notes and References

1. If Adam and Eve had not sinned, they and their children would never have experienced death. See Louis Berkhof, *Systematic Theology* (reprint ed., Grand Rapids: Eerdmans Publishing Company, 1969), pp. 669-671.

2. Jay E. Adams, *Shepherding God's Flock*, Vol. 1 (Phillipsburg, New Jersey: Presbyterian and Reformed Publishing Company, 1974), pp. 128-156.

CHAPTER 7

Abortion: The Killing Fields

"Then the Lord spoke to Moses, saying, 'Again, you shall say to the children of Israel: "Whoever of the children of Israel, or of the strangers who sojourn in Israel, who gives any of his descendants to Molech, he shall surely be put to death. The people of the land shall stone him with stones. I will set My face against that man, and will cut him off from his people, because he has given some of his descendants to Molech, to defile My sanctuary and profane My holy name. And if the people of the land should in any way hide their eyes from the man, when he gives some of his descendants to Molech, and they do not kill him, then I will set My face against that man and against his family; and I will cut him off from his people, and all who prostitute themselves with him to commit harlotry with Molech"'" (Leviticus 20:1-5).*

Someone once said, "Civilization is a thin veneer over barbarism." He was wrong! There is no veneer!

In our day, stoning or any form of capital punishment is "inhumane," while abortion is "sound medical practice."[1] Murderers are slapped on the hand and set free to "do their thing." Meanwhile, babies both within the womb and after birth are killed.

Let us be clear here. The Supreme Court in its 1973 decision allowed for abortion *at any time during pregnancy.* Through the sixth month, the decision was left solely to the woman and her physician. After the sixth month, state governments could regulate abortion *if they chose to do so*!

Maybe there once was a veneer. Now, what was once done in secret has been brought to the light of "sound medical practice."

Many Christians are "turned off" by some descriptions in the Old Testament. These include God's actions, as well as the actions of men. The passage above, however, describes both God and man as they always are and always have been. This passage is not "old hat" to be cast aside. It is all too relevant today.

Molech was a god of the Ammonites to whom children were "passed through the fire." That is, they were sacrificed. Sacrifices are made to gods to obtain their favor and to gain prosperity, pleasure, and power.

Is abortion any different? More to the point -- is abortion not child sacrifice? The reasons for abortion are clear. People want sexual pleasure (often as fornication and adultery) without the biological consequences. People want prosperity, but children cost a lot of money, and they interfere with activities that give power and prestige.

Children cause many inconveniences to parents. Children require that women be homebound "slaves" (according to liberals). Thus, Molech is alive and well today. People do not believe that some deity will reward them for their child sacrifice, but they believe that they will gain rewards by the destruction of their children.

Let's be sure about God's position in this passage. Not only was the one who gave the child to be sacrificed to be stoned to death, but anyone who knew of the act and allowed it to go unpunished ("hid their eyes"). God's judgment rested not only upon the person, but upon his family. Today, the large majority of our society "hides its eyes" while the government and the medical profession officially commits child sacrifice. Far worse, most who call themselves "Christians" condone the practice. (They may not actually be Christians, as we will see.) And -- physicians are the priests who commit this sacrifice.

The people of the United States ought to be frightened! God has not changed. He is *the same yesterday, today and forever" (Hebrews 13:8)*. He will bring His judgments upon us.

Some Gruesome Statistics

Since the passage of *Roe v. Wade* in 1973, there have been more than 30 million abortions in the United States. (Estimates world-wide range from 100-200 million, but few nations have accurate or efficient reporting of these numbers.) Almost one-third of all pregnancies end in abortion. In some large cities, however, the number of abortions *exceeds* live births. Twenty-six percent of women who have abortions are less than 20 years of age, 33 percent are 20-24 years of age, and 41 percent are over 25 years of age.

The time of pregnancy when abortions are performed denotes the reality of this terrible slaughter. In 1987, 51 percent were performed at 8 weeks of age or earlier and 39 percent at 9-12 weeks.[2] Some 3.6 percent were performed from 16-20 weeks when infants are not yet viable, but are able to live for a few minutes and make struggling motions to live (if they are not killed or dismembered by the abortion process). Some 0.6 percent were performed at or after 20 weeks, when all babies are potentially viable and some have been "saved" when born prematurely.

These latter figures from 1987 are more striking, however, if they are presented numerically. The 3.6 percent is 55,910 abortions and 0.6 percent is 9,030. In other words, over nine thousand babies are aborted who are otherwise viable at the time that they are killed!

Figures that are used to promote abortion concern women who had to seek and sometimes died from "back-alley" abortions. Bernard Nathanson, a former leader for abortion "rights" and now an activist against abortion, has said how they arrived at these "statistics."[3]

> "I confess that I knew that the figures were totally false and I suppose the others did too if they stopped to think of it. But in the 'morality' of our revolution it was a *useful* figure, widely accepted, so why go out or our way to correct it with honest statistics?"

The actual numbers of maternal deaths from illegal abortions from the mid-1950s to the mid-1960s ranged between 70 and 135 each year.[4] The total number of illegal abortions prior to its legalization was not reported. If, however, this number of deaths is compared to the total number of illegal abortions in Canada and Great Britain, then the total number of abortions in the United States was approximately 100,000 per year. This number is also confirmed by projecting back the increased number of abortions *after legalization* in those countries.

We could go on *ad nauseam* (both in repetition and grisly descriptions), but these statistics should be sufficient to give an overview of the problem and its history.

Does Life Begin at Conception?

This question ought to be more carefully phrased, "Does *individual human* life begin at conception?" Phrased as it is above, its intent is easily side-stepped with the comment that life, even human life, is a continuum. Individual human life, however, has a beginning and an end. Pro-abortionists try to sidestep the issue by saying that the determination of the beginning of individual human life is not important. Justice Blackmun stated in *Roe v. Wade*, "We need not resolve the question of when life begins."

But Christians ought not to lose their focus. *The most important question concerning abortion is, "When does individual human life begin?"*

The Bible is clear. First, conception is linked to the life of the individual after birth. *"She (Eve) conceived and bore Cain" (Genesis 4:1).* Similarly, other a named mothers "conceived and bore" named children (Genesis 4:1, 17; 21:2; 29:32, 33, 35; 30:5, 19, 23; 38:3,4). Some forty times Scripture makes the statement that the life of a person started with conception in the mother. This link clearly states that conception, and not birth, is the beginning of individual human life.

Second, the Bible portrays God's activity in the development of the person during gestation. The following is probably the best known example.

"For you have formed my inward parts;

You have covered me in my mother's womb.
I will praise You,
*   for I am fearfully and wonderfully made;*
Marvelous are Your works,
And that my soul knows very well.
My frame was not hidden from You,
When I was made in secret,
And skillfully wrought in the lowest parts of the earth.
Your eyes saw my substance, being yet unformed.
And in Your book they all were written,
The days fashioned for me,
When as yet there were none of them"
(Psalm 139:13-16).

The baby becomes "formed," that is, he has a clear identity as a human being, amazingly early in gestation. At seven and one-half weeks after conception, brain activity is present. At eight weeks, his fingerprints (that will never change throughout his life) are present. He is clearly recognizable as human and cannot be confused with any other species of life. At ten weeks, the baby can squint, swallow, move his tongue, and the sex hormones are present.

Thus, God's vision of "unformed substance" implies the first few days and weeks of existence. On this basis, the passage can be applied even earlier in gestation than many Christians who have used this passage may have considered.

Third, God speaks of the unborn as persons whose lives He has planned. We have seen one instance already (Psalm 139:16). Another concerns the prophet Jeremiah.

"Before I formed you in the womb I knew you;
Before you were born I sanctified you;
And I ordained you a prophet to the nations"
(Jeremiah 1:5).

He holds David responsible for the inherited sin of Adam and Eve.

"Behold, I was brought forth in iniquity,

And in sin my mother conceived me" (Psalm 51:5).

Thus, God considers the unborn from the time of conception to be fully a person.

Fourth, only human beings can be filled with the Holy Spirit. The angel spoke to Zacharias that his son, whom we call "John the Baptist," would *"be filled with the Holy Spirit, even from his mother's womb" (Luke 1:15).* During his gestation this special union was evident when *"the babe leaped in [Elizabeth's] womb" (Luke 1:41).*

This fourth reason is evident in the major orthodox arguments concerning ensoulement.[5] Basically, there are two positions. *Creationism* (to be distinguished from God's original creation of all things) states that the soul is specially created by God at the moment of conception. *Traducianism* states that the soul of the offspring is imparted from his parents. *Both positions agree that the soul is present at the moment of conception.* They differ only on how it comes into being.

Science really offers no reasonable time of transition for the developing baby to become a "person" either. *There is no logical or compelling development from conception to birth that would even suggest, much less authenticate, that the unborn's status had changed from a non-person to a person.* The entire process involves constant change and the development of new abilities of the developing baby. Of course, the materialist (one who denies the reality of the spiritual world) might link the definition of a person with the brain. Even this organ, however, undergoes constant change from the time of conception to the time of birth. After birth the brain continues to develop and change throughout life.

Abortion Is a Symptom

A primary principle for medical practice is the distinction between symptoms and diseases. For example, a cough may indicate pneumonia, sinusitis, lung cancer, tuberculosis, or any number of other diseases. The same principle applies here. Abortion is not the disease; it is a symptom. The disease is "secular humanism," as it is commonly referred to. More specifically, it is an anti-God mentality that has no standard of right and wrong. The cure is not only to pass laws that prohibit abortion. The cure is regeneration or being "born again." When that happens, a person is changed from being a secular humanist to a Bible believer.

First, *being anti-abortion is a non-negotiable ethic for true Christians.* The practice is totally against the character of God and His design for the human race. Everywhere God is described as the God of life, not of death. We have seen in an earlier chapter that the true definition of life is communion with God. Nowhere is the death of innocent people a Biblical solution to any problem.

Further, He describes Himself as the God of the fatherless and calls for the special care of the fatherless (Deuteronomy 14:29; Isaiah 1:17; James 1:27).[6] For sure, today's unborn children are fatherless. The Supreme Court in its *Roe v. Wade* decision of 1973 disallowed the father's having any right to say what is or is not done with the unborn baby. Not only does this law apply to babies conceived out of wedlock, but *those conceived within marriage as well.* Thus, the heart of marriage can be ripped out along with the unborn baby. This destruction of marriage was the reason that God's judgment was applied to families as well as individuals (Leviticus 20:5).

The unborn are among the most defenseless of people. They cannot voice protest. They cannot run away from danger, as is clearly and violently portrayed in the video, "The Silent Scream."

By contrast, God designed the unborn to be the most protected. Their nourishment is constant and dependable. Their environment is quite comfortable and unchanging. They do not have to interact with people and be hurt by them. They are physically well-protected, often so well that the mother can be seriously injured and they are not.

Few things are as "unnatural" as abortion. Its presence is a symptom of a society that is far "down the tubes." Perhaps, only such things as homosexuality, incest, pedophilia, and bestiality are further down. It is unthinkable that a child of God could favor its practice in any way. More specifically, it is indefensible Biblically.

Theologically, an anti-abortion position cannot be a test of orthodoxy. That is, it cannot be a test of whether a person is a true Christian or not. I do believe, however, that a pro-abortion position seriously brings into a question the regenerated status of a person's mind. A denial of the clear character of God and His laws is inconsistent for those who claim to be His children.

Abortion and the Family

We should understand that abortion represents as much, if not more so, a destruction of the family as destruction of human life. The most intimate human relationship is the "one flesh" nature of husband and wife (Genesis 2:24b; Matthew 19:1-10). The highest call for one human to care for another is that the husband should love his wife *"just as Christ also loved the church and gave himself for it" (Ephesians 5:25)* and to "nourish and cherish" her as he does his own body (Ephesians 5:28-29). The negative statement of this oneness is, of course, the Seventh Commandment: *"Thou shalt not commit adultery" (Exodus 20:14).*

Most abortions are the "cure" for pregnancies that are a result of sexual promiscuity. The extent of this promiscuity is directly correlated to the value place upon God's design of sexuality for marriage. Certainly, the most "Christian" society will have some sexual immorality, but not openly and as prevalent as the one in which the family has been devalued. Both the man and the woman who are promiscuous make the statement that the limitation of sexuality to marriage is unimportant. Abortion, the destruction of the life created by that union, is a further denial of the value of the family into which the child would have been brought. The pregnancy that results from promiscuity does not have to end in abortion. The baby could be placed for adoption. Thus, abortion is not a consequence of promiscuity but an additional statement that the raising of a child in a family is unimportant. In reality, the mother acts in a way that considers her unborn child to be better off dead than being raised in a family!

Abortion causes further decline in the family. The stressed

mother may at times think toward her children, "I could have aborted you and avoided this trouble." Heaven forbid, but some even voice this thought! Husbands and wives are less fearful of adultery, knowing that abortion is an efficient and hidden "backup" to a consequent pregnancy. Further, as the number of children increases in a family, the temptation increases to prevent further stress on the family budget by the abortion of the next child.

Abortion assists the state in its control of the family. The Biblical pattern is for grown children to take care of their parents when they are no longer able to take of themselves (Mark 7:6-13). With no children, the elderly must depend upon the state to care for them, if they have not made sufficient provision for themselves (and most have not). Even with one or two children, the burden upon so few might be more than they are able to handle along with their own financial responsibilities.

Abortion: The Watershed Issue

A watershed is the dividing line for an issue. The legalization of abortion is the watershed to the protection of all human life. The Nazi atrocities began with abortion a decade or more before the concentration camps and gas chambers. The Germans were desensitized that some humans were disposable, inconvenient, and interfered with personal and national hopes for prosperity.

Why are the unborn the first to be destroyed? Perhaps, they are the most defenseless. Perhaps, they are hidden from view and are disposed of without anyone ever having to visualize them. Perhaps, their disposal is relatively simple. For sure, they are sometimes described as "a mass of cells" that do not look "human." For sure, a pregnancy is a considerable inconvenience for a woman physically, socially, and financially. For sure, a pregnancy is sometimes an embarrassment when it is the result of sexual promiscuity. For sure, some talk of a world population that is outgrowing its resources. (See Chapter 9.) For sure, there are other reasons.

The people of the United States do not generally believe

that what happened in Nazi Germany can happen here. We are a "civilized" country, perhaps the most civilized country in the history of the world. The trends of history and of logic, however, belie this belief. The wanton destruction of human life that could occur in a relatively short time, given the right circumstances, staggers the imagination. Likely, only the checks and balances of our federal and state governments have slowed the process from a rapid downhill slide. We are, however, beginning to see the loosening of controls over the protection of the comatose, the deformed, the retarded and others who are "burdens" to society. Many medical ethicists see no difference between allowing someone to die from the natural course of his illness and giving him a lethal injection.

Conservative Christians are in the most danger from this downhill slide. "Separation of church and state" has become a fixture in modern society, politics, and law. Of course, its common meaning is a distortion of the constitutional framers' intent. Nevertheless, perhaps the strongest movement in the United States is the restriction of anything Christian or Biblical to the private sphere. What ought to be apparent is that historically, the restriction of ideological freedom is followed by physical restriction (the ghetto) and that followed by persecution. Most people know of the murder of millions of Jews in Nazi Germany. What few realize is that millions of non-Jews were murdered as well.

Thus, abortion may be the precedent for the persecution of Christians. We are not just fighting for the right to life of the unborn. We are engaged in a fight for the right to life of Christians. Unfortunately, few Christians are concerned, because they have bought the lie of separation of church and state (official policy of some major denominations) and the supposed civilization of the United States. The legalization of abortion desensitizes people to the killing of human life. It opens the door to killing other categories of humans who are an inconvenience, expense or embarrassment. The other dominoes will begin to fall if Biblical reformation does not occur. There is no other hope, because there is no other moral base that establishes the value of human life and that motivates people to make the necessary effort to reconstruct society.

The Social Consequences of Abortion

Babies, children, and the adults that they become are a source of knowledge and wealth for a society. Unfortunately, some think that the larger the population, the fewer the resources that are available on a per capita basis. (Again, see Chapter 9.) What is not considered are the resources of the growing population, especially in an industrial society. First, the goods and services necessary to raise these children to adulthood are considerable. Pregnant women have to have special clothes and medical care. Babies and children need clothes, food and bigger houses. When they enter school, they need supplies and teachers. All these items create industries and jobs for large numbers of people.

By the time the children start school, they become buyers themselves. Their early impact may not be great, but the spendable income of today's teenagers is staggering. Then, when they marry and have their own children, they compound the goods and services necessary. As they enter the work force, they become producers. Their talents and knowledge increase efficiency and production. And, they become taxpayers!

Dr. Allan Carlson used such items to calculate the lost productivity for these aborted children, assuming that the current numbers of abortions continue.[7] By the year 2000, some 40 million babies will have been aborted. In the year 2025, their economic impact (all figures are in 1984 dollars) would have totaled $1.45 trillion *in that year alone*. Figuring 20 percent in federal taxes of one sort or another, a total of $291 billion would not be realized. His figures for *those already aborted* are a total impact of $636 billion and taxes of $127 billion in the year 2010. He has called this loss, "The Malthusian Deficit."

It is ironic that babies are being aborted because of their financial liability to families and to the nation. These are short-term savings, if they are savings at all. In the long run, abortions are a considerable loss of human resources and productivity to a nation. As Christians, we should adopt the axiom that *any violation of God's laws has a severe economic consequence*

in the long run. Abortion in itself is heinous, but its consequences extend far beyond the act alone. *"The wages of sin is
death" (Romans 6:23)* -- both directly to the unborn child and
indirectly to the economic and social health of a nation.

CHAPTER SUMMARY

1. Modern "civilization" practices a form of child-sacrifice by
   its widespread practice of abortion.
2. The whole of society shares in guilt and condemnation
   before God for the practice of abortion.
3. There are 1.3 million abortions each year in the United
   States. Over 9,000 of these are after the age of viability!
4. Prior to the legalization of abortion, there were only 1/10
   the number of current abortions.
5. The Bible is clear that individual human life begins at
   conception. Conception is linked to the subsequent named
   individual. God is active in the development of the unborn,
   God speaks of the unborn as persons, and the unborn can
   be filled with the Holy Spirit.
6. Orthodox Protestant theologians have long believed that
   the soul is present at conception.
7. Being anti-abortion is a non-negotiable ethic for the Christian.
8. Abortion represents the destruction of the family as much
   as the destruction of a life.
9. The legalization of abortion increases the fragmentation of
   the family.
10. Abortion is a watershed issue for the sanctity of all human
    life. When it becomes legal, other forms of killing follow.
11. Abortion is a possible precedent for the persecution of
    Christians.
12. The economic loss to a society from abortion is severe.

Notes and References

1. "Sound medical practice" is a phrase that the American Medical Association and other medical organizations have used in defense of legalized
abortion.

2. Stanley K. Henshaw *et al.*, "Characteristics of U. S. Women Having

Abortions, 1987," *Family Planning Perspectives* 23 (March/April 1991), pp. 75-81.

3. Ian Gentles, "Abortion, Law and Human Behavior," *The Human Life Review*, 13 (Spring 1987), pp. 68-87.

4. *Ibid.*

5. Ensoulement is the time at which and method by which the soul is joined to the body.

6. Curt Young, formerly Executive Director of the national Christian Action Council, first made me aware that *Roe v. Wade* had the effect of making all children legally fatherless while in the womb.

7. Allan Carlson, "The Malthusian Budget Deficit," *The Human Life Review*, 11 (Summer 1985), pp. 35-47.

CHAPTER 8

Who Are My Mother and Father?

"After these things the word of the LORD came to Abram in a vision, saying, 'Do not be afraid, Abram. I am your shield, your exceedingly great reward.' But Abram said, 'Lord GOD, what will You give me, seeing I go childless, and the heir of my house is Eliezer of Damascus?' Then Abram said, 'Look, You have given me no offspring; indeed one born in my house is my heir!' And behold, the word of the LORD came to him, saying, 'This one shall not be your heir, but one who will come from your own body shall be your heir.'

"Now Sarai, Abram's wife, had borne him no children. And she had an Egyptian maidservant whose name was Hagar. So Sarai said to Abram, 'See now, the LORD has restrained me from bearing children. Please, go in to my maid; perhaps I shall obtain children by her.' And Abram heeded the voice of Sarai.... So he went in to Hagar, and she conceived.

"Then Abraham fell on his face and laughed, and said in his heart, 'Shall a child be born to a man who is one hundred years old? And shall Sarah, who is ninety years old, bear a child?'

"Therefore Sarah laughed within herself, saying, 'After I have grown old, shall I have pleasure, my lord being old also?'

"And the LORD visited Sarah as He had said, and the LORD did for Sarah as He had spoken. For Sarah conceived and bore Abraham a son in his old age, at the set time of which God had spoken to him" (Genesis 15:1-4; 16:1,2,4; 17:17; 18:12; 21:1-2).

Efforts to have children in spite of a couple's infertility did not begin with artificial insemination and surrogate mothers! Abraham and Sarah became impatient with God and attempted to fulfill His promise in their own way.

However, when man attempts to circumvent God's designs, the results are always disastrous. In this Biblical event, bitter enmity developed between Sarah and Hagar, and eventually, Hagar and Ishmael were banished from their home (Genesis 21:8-21). And, this enmity continued between Abraham's and Ishmael's descendants (Psalm 83:6), and it continues to this day!

Further, sin is always multiplied in its fruit. Abraham and Sarah attempted a simple solution that backfired into family and international strife. The sexual sins of our day are being compounded in a similar way. Most attempts to solve problems of infertility are sinful and will continue to reap ugly fruit. For example, it is possible for children to have five different "parents." The egg and sperm can come from a man and woman with conception (fertilization) occurring *in vitro*. Then, the embryo can be placed in the womb of a surrogate mother, who then carries and delivers the baby for a yet different couple, who adopt the newborn baby. Biologically, that child would have difficulty knowing the answer to the question, "Who are my mother and father?"

Sin May Cause Infertility

It is estimated that more than one in six couples in the United States is infertile and more than a million seek help for this problem from doctors and clinics each year. At first glance, these clinics seem to provide a much-needed service for a difficult problem. However, this perception is only partially true, as many causes of infertility are sin-related.

Two extremes should be avoided. One extreme is that all problems of infertility are a direct result of sin. The other extreme is that all problems of infertility are not related to sin (personal guilt of either the man or the woman). My belief is that too little attention has been directed to the latter. Infertile couples seem to be "lumped" together as a group who are "victims." Let us then review the known causes of infertility related to personal sin.

Sexually Transmitted Diseases (STDs). Within the last twenty years, the number of infertile couples has tripled. Research indicates that a large portion of the cause of this increase lies with the "sexual revolution." Promiscuity has caused millions of cases of STDs that scar and destroy delicate reproductive organs, preventing fertilization and implantation (the embedding of the embryo into the womb to establish its life support from its mother).

In addition, STDs may lead to ectopic pregnancies, because conditions in the Fallopian tube allow the tiny sperm to pass on their way to fertilize the egg but will not allow the much larger fertilized egg to pass in the opposite direction to the uterus, where it would become implanted. The embryo may then implant within the abdomen (abdominal pregnancy) or in the Fallopian tube (tubal pregnancy). As the embryo grows, tissues are torn and severe bleeding occurs, necessitating surgical removal of the embryo and tube to prevent the mother from bleeding to death. A live birth from such a pregnancy is extremely rare, and then only by abdominal surgery.

Spontaneous abortions (miscarriages) occur when a fertilized egg fails to implant because the lining of the womb is inflamed or scarred from an STD. While implantation normally occurs within ten days of conception, a woman's menstrual period occurs fourteen days after ovulation (the expulsion of the egg from the ovary). Thus, the failure of implantation will not prolong the onset of her next menstrual period, so that she will never know that she had conceived!

Abortion. Demand for artificial reproduction is increased, because babies have been aborted instead of being placed for adoption. These aborted (1.5 million per year) would almost certainly be sufficient to provide children for all infertile couples who wanted them. Thus, adoption could eliminate the need for all forms of artificial reproduction with their inherent technical and moral problems.

Postponed childbirth. With many women seeking careers outside the home, they are postponing childbirth. The older a couple is, however, when they attempt to have children, the more likely that infertility may occur or that a child will be born with congenital deformities. The average time for a woman over 35 years of age to conceive is two years, as opposed to six months for younger women. The incidence of genetic abnormalities increases as age increases in both men and women.

Scientism. This word (as I am using it here) denotes the scientific attitude that all areas of knowledge should be investigated and that any procedure that can be done should be done, regardless of its morality or immorality. Scientists and physicians have little regard for the sanctity of marriage, while they have great regard for their own technical ability. "If it can be done, it should be done." Thus, lesbians are impregnated so they can have their "own" children. The only limit on what physicians and scientists will or will not do seems to be their technical ability, available funding, and an occasional prohibiting regulation or law.

Without the cooperation of physicians, the sexual revolution may not have occurred or certainly would have been limited in its extent and effect. Without reliable birth control and abortion, there would have been a greater reluctance to seek sexual relationships outside of marriage. Such medical cooperation is representative of this amoral scientism that places no restriction on its own or those who seek its services.

Consequences of Abortion. Abortion can prevent future conceptions because reproductive organs may be permanently damaged by the procedures that are used. The more times that a woman has an abortion, the greater the likelihood that she will have such damage. Also, the guilt, anxiety and interpersonal conflicts that often result from abortion can cause impotence or frigidity - both potential causes of infertility.

For pastors and others who counsel infertile couples, the cause(s) of the infertility ought to be explored. One or both spouses may be infertile for one of the above reasons. This information should be brought to light, not to condemn them or even to preclude their seeking medical help for their infertility (within Biblical limits), but to be sure that such sin has been repented of and for the couple to know when they are reaping what they have sown, in order to be instructed thereby in God's

school of suffering. Compassion is not the only needed response to infertile couples.

The Unity of the Husband and Wife

Biblical unity is the major principle for artificial reproduction. First, *the unity of the husband and wife is not dependent
on the presence of children.* In fact, marriages that last a
normal lifetime span more years without children than they do
with them. When infertile couples complain, "We need a child
to complete our marriage," they have misunderstood the Biblical concept of marriage. Certainly, God's original general
design is for children to be born to and raised by married
couples. This design, however, is for the "nurture and admonition" of the children primarily and the fulfillment of the marriage secondarily.

Second, *the egg and sperm are biological representatives of
this unity.*

> "When one understands the 'one flesh' concept in
> marriage as a holy sexual unity, from which, in normal
> situations and at certain times, new individuals may
> find their beginnings, then the active insinuation of
> another individual's active genetic potential and person-
> al history into that unity seems to be disruptive. The
> woman is now engaged with someone else (anonymous-
> ly and sexlessly) in bringing a new life into that unity.
> The female part of carrying, and delivering one whom
> God ordains to be naturally the result of the unity....
> When one of the partners uses his or her individual
> portion of the one-flesh sexuality to 'father' or 'mother'
> a new individual outside of their particular male-female
> unity, it seems to me, in that instance, to be destroying
> the one-flesh concept of that partnership."[1]

Third, *the use of donor sperm likely constitutes adultery.*
Many theologians readily dismiss adultery in this context. This
dismissal, however, is tenuous at best. Christ stated clearly
that adultery can be committed in one's heart (Matthew 5:27-

28), but overt adultery involves physical contact. In our present context, the presence of a substance (semen) from the sexual organs of a man, obtained by a sexual act (masturbation), and placed within the sexual organs of a woman certainly approaches adultery. While whole persons are not intimate in the procedure, the organs and tissues involved certainly are those that are involved in sexual intercourse.

Further, masturbation (to obtain sperm) is often performed as an act of sexual fantasy, usually with pornography. Such acts are clearly immoral (Matthew 5:27-30). While the woman in whom the semen is placed is not as likely to have adulterous thoughts (toward the donor), she may. The fact that most donors are young, often medical students, and that local papers run pictures of handsome men to attract donors, increases her temptation. Thus, the mental act of adultery may occur in both the donor and the recipient.

A donor egg from a woman other than the wife is less problematic than sperm because the egg is obtained by purely technical means, rather than a sexual act as in masturbation. Nevertheless, a donor egg violates the unity of marriage as an outside agent that invades and becomes a permanent part of the marriage in the form of the child conceived.

Important to this discussion is the moral significance of semen and eggs *per se*. They are unique bodily tissues, as they have the potential to unite and procreate a person with an eternal soul. Even if the soul of this new person is not present until conception (see creationism and traducianism in Chapter 7), the genes within them carry personal characteristics of the biological mother and father. This additional personal element brings the use of donor gametes even closer to its being an act of adultery.

For all these reasons, the use of sperm or eggs from donors is unbiblical. Not only is an inequality introduced into the marriage, but the inequality itself is associated with the sexual organs. The closeness of artificial insemination with donor sperm to the act of adultery ought to be sufficient for Christians to proscribe it.

Fertilization Methods

Artificial Insemination (AI). The sperm of the husband or a donor is placed directly into the woman's vagina or into her uterus. Indications for AI include a low sperm count or retrograde ejaculation in the husband or physical problems that prevent sexual intercourse. Also, the biochemical conditions of the wife's vagina may be hostile to her husband's sperm. Only rarely today is the husband's sperm used to inseminate his wife, mostly because the problems that cause his infertility (usually a low sperm count) also preclude his sperm being used to inseminate his wife.

In Vitro Fertilization (IVF). Eggs are taken from a woman's ovary through a laparoscope (lighted tube placed into her abdomen) and transferred to a specially prepared Petri dish (not test tubes) along with sperm. After fertilization occurs, the egg is allowed to multiply from one cell (the zygote) to 4-8 cells and then placed into the woman's uterus, where it will become implanted into the wall of the uterus. As might be expected, this procedure is fraught with potential problems, reflected in its 12-15 percent success rate in producing a live, healthy baby.

Fortunately, *in vitro* centers work almost exclusively with married couples. Thus, the unity of the marriage is preserved. (These centers' choice was a practical decision, not a moral choice.) The greatest moral problem with IVF is that 3-5 eggs are usually fertilized. Those that appear "abnormal" under the microscope are discarded. Since individual human life begins at conception, this method is a disposal of human lives. Thus, as Christians, we must require that all fertilized eggs be given the chance for survival by their being placed back into the woman.[2]

Freezing of embryos. Sometimes embryos are frozen, to be used later in the same couple if a successful pregnancy does not occur initially. In other situations, the embryos are "banked," to be used by another couple whose infertility problems cannot be overcome by *in vitro* fertilization.

We must condemn the freezing of embryos in both cases. The freezing process itself destroys many of them. Then, if the present attempt at *in vitro* fertilization is successful, the embryos may be discarded or used for experimentation. Even with continued preservation, their legal status is unresolved. Do they belong to the original couple? Do they belong to the physicians or laboratory that maintains them? Surely, the placing of humans in such a precarious existence is prohibited for those who are made in the image of God!

Surrogate Mothers. Here, a fertilized egg is placed into a woman who agrees to carry the baby to term, and after his birth, give it to another couple for adoption. Earlier, we listed five possibilities that might occur with this method. This procedure must be condemned mostly for reasons that have already been presented. There are, however, some that are unique.

First, the surrogate is motivated by the money she is to receive. In essence, human life is negotiated for a "price." Thus, human life becomes a commercial product, opening the door to all the potential abuses of commercialization, such as broken contracts, black markets, price wars and degrading advertising.

Second, the process violates "motherhood." It is clear that maternal-infant bonding is real (see below). It is an instinctive result for two humans who share themselves intimately with each other for nine months. With surrogate mothers, however, this bonding is broken immediately upon the delivery of the baby. It is not easily given up, as has been seen in the famous New Jersey case. Surrogate mothers differ from other adoptions, because the latter occur in unplanned pregnancies and are attempts to make the most out of difficult situations. Surrogate contracts *create* the situations wherein difficulties may occur.

The Kinsman-Redeemer and the Levirate[3]

In discussions of reproduction alternatives, Old Testament references to the kinsman-redeemer and the levirate are relevant (Deuteronomy 25:5-10). The purpose of these directives was the continuance of the family name and the retention of family property. The marriage of those "related by blood or by marriage, marriage and sexual union by a widow or a widower to in-laws was considered incest --- except in this one instance."

If a woman's husband died without children, she was permitted "to marry her next of kin in order to raise up a family to bear the name of the dead man."

For example, it was Onan's responsibility to marry Tamar to continue the name and property of his brother, Er (Genesis 38:8-10). His sin was his failure to impregnate her when he "wasted his seed on the ground." Tamar's subsequent act to seduce her father-in-law was "a desperate act of a woman who desired children from the same stock as her husband" and *not* a fulfillment of the levirate obligation.

The other example of this situation in the Old Testament involved Ruth and Boaz. Since she did not have a brother-in-law to act as a levirate (Ruth 1:11-12), the responsibility fell to the "kinsman-redeemer," her closest relative. In her situation, the "close relative" passed his responsibility to Boaz, the next closest relative.

These Biblical exceptions to the normal principles for marriage and inheritance, however, do not justify modern reproductive methods. First, these special circumstances called for *the actual marriage* of the man and woman, preserving the psycho-physical unity of marriage, with its procreation of children. Second, the levirate and kinsman-redeemer are the only exceptions to the procreation of children outside the norm in the entire Bible. Exceptions to God's Word are never our prerogative. "Only He can modify his own directives for His good purposes."[4]

The Conflict of Compassion and Principle

Those who oppose reproductive methods that use donor sperm or eggs are often accused of lacking compassion for the plight of the infertile couple. Indeed, the intensity with which that challenge is issued is almost impossible to overcome by reason alone. Christians, however, must learn to have their feelings, especially those that are more intense, to be guided by the Word of God, not the undirected force of those feelings alone. Admittedly, with intense emotions, submission to God's Word is not easy. Nevertheless, that is the task to which God calls us.

Indeed, we have already demonstrated that the prevalence of infertility is proportional to the sexual sins of our society. *On that basis alone* many couples are only experiencing the consequences of their sin. *Where was their earlier passion for the family as God designed it and for the practice of His Law?* Let us be clear that compassion without clear vision and Biblical direction is nothing more than free-floating sentimentalism.

What about those couples in whom there is no evidence of sin-caused infertility? Again, compassion without direction only causes greater harm and violates God's design.

Certainly their plight is a difficult one. Couples usually marry in anticipation of the joy of having their own children. When it doesn't happen, bitterness, disappointment, and years of medical procedures and "work ups" follow. Couples with children are often unaware of the prevalence of infertile couples and are insensitive to their situation, one that is only intensified with today's paucity of babies that are available for adoption.

Beyond the principles already presented, however, is another aspect. We moderns are quite impatient to accept God's design for our lives. Infertility is one such example. Sometimes we hear a childless woman say, "I would do anything for a child." Does that mean that she would steal? Kill? Commit adultery? She said *anything*! More accurately, she should say, "I will do *anything* consistent with God's will as revealed in the Bible to have a child." Indeed, she can do anything within that framework. Medical workups and procedures, as well as adoption proceedings, are certainly permissible within the Biblical principles already stated. If, however, the couple remains childless, they must accept the completeness of their marriage without children and seek other avenues to pursue God's call on their lives.

The attitude of childless couples often reflects an unwillingness to accept this situation, and compassion for their situation often blinds others to its presence. God even warns about this difficulty.

"There are three things that are never satisfied,
Four things never say, 'It is enough':
The grave,

The barren womb,
The earth that is not satisfied with water,
And the fire that never says, 'It is enough'"
(Proverbs 30:15-16).

A comparison may help us to understand that the noble and Biblical desire of parenthood can be inordinate.

"On what rational ground is it urged that while sexual desires ought not to be indulged at will, parental desires may be? And are the results of indulgence later likely to be quite different, in their total effect on the personality, from those which are known to follow the former? If we persuade ourselves that because we want a thing so much it must be right for us to have it, do we not thereby reject in principle, though perhaps unwittingly, the very idea of limitation, acceptance, of a given providential order and social frame --- in a word, the creatureliness of man?"[5]

Thus, we need to extend compassion and be sensitive to infertile couples, but we must not ever allow compassion to go beyond the bounds of God's principles. To do so is to move beyond any basis for the determination of right and wrong.

More on the Morality of In Vitro *Fertilization*

A prohibition of *in vitro* fertilization does not seem warranted when Biblical criteria are followed. That is, the sperm and eggs come from a husband and wife who are married to each other, all embryos are placed back into the woman, induced abortion is not part of the protocol, and amniocentesis is not planned (except when it is intended to obtain information to help a distressed baby *in utero*). There are, however, some considerations that make the IVF undesirable and possibly unwarranted.

1) The procedure is costly, being $5,000-$10,000 per procedure, with five attempts usually needed to produce one successful pregnancy. 2) The impetus for this procedure has been increased by sexual immorality. 3) It would be extremely difficult for the couple to maintain moral thoughts and behavior throughout this trying ordeal. 4) Since more than one egg must

be fertilized for the procedure to be practical, then usually more than one embryo is lost with each procedure. (Even with natural procreation, however, 50 percent or more of embryos may be lost.) 5) If Christians are successful to stop abortions, then adoptions could be a viable alternative to IVF.

On the one hand, I believe that these arguments are sufficient to advocate that this procedure should be abandoned. On the other hand, no one condition or all together have a Biblical basis sufficient to establish an inviolate Biblical ethic to prohibit IVF. Christians who consider this option would do well to seek the counsel of their pastors and church leaders.

Artificial Wombs

Apart from the brief period of time (less than 24 hours) that the embryo is outside its mother in IVF, artificial wombs are not yet possible. Some believe that they never will be. I am, however, reluctant to take that position considering the technical achievements of modern science. At any rate we ought to consider the ethics of the possibility. Briefly and bluntly, *no womb is acceptable other than that of the genetic mother.*

In effect, parenting begins before birth. The nutrition of the mother affects the developing infant for better or worse. Sleep patterns are established according to the mother's routines. The child's own nervous system senses the emotions of its mother and even receives into its own bloodstream the hormones associated with these emotions. Even the father of the child affects the infant, because he is the most significant emotional factor in the mother's life. Her moods will be deeply affected by how he treats her. Thus, the provisions of food, shelter and education have begun before birth. In modern language, it is called "maternal-infant bonding." It is, however, nothing less than parenting before birth.

This parenting obviously cannot be carried out by some machine. Neither can it be carried out by some animal, as some have proposed them to be used as artificial wombs. We must condemn such proposals as violations of God's ordained plan for families.

One exception would be the temporary removal of a de-

veloping baby for the purposes of therapy (e.g., correcting
some defect that might cause it to die before birth).

Such technology, along with an increasing role for state
government, may destroy any reality in "parenting." Picture *in
vitro* fertilization with sperm and egg from "banks," followed
by a "pregnancy" in a robotic or animal womb. The "product
of conception," then, could be "decanted" directly into a 24-
hour day-care center staffed by state-trained, state-paid "professionals." *Brave New World*, you are well on your way to realization!

CHAPTER SUMMARY

1. Man's attempts to circumvent God's ordained pattern of
   procreation through families did not begin with the modern
   era.
2. Sin always causes more problems than man is able to
   solve, even with his most sophisticated technology.
3. The number of infertile couples has tripled in the past two
   decades.
4. Personal sins have accounted for this increase. These
   include sexually transmitted diseases, postponed childbirth,
   scientism, and the consequences of abortion.
5. Abortion kills 1.5 million babies per year that could be
   available for adoption.
6. The major Biblical principle for reproductive issues is the
   unity of the husband and wife.
7. This unity prohibits the use of sperm or eggs that come
   from donors.
8. Sperm for artificial insemination (donor) are obtained by
   masturbation, an immoral act.
9. Artificial insemination may use the husband's sperm, but
   this method is rarely performed.
10. *In vitro* fertilization requires the fertilization of several
    eggs. All these should be transferred to the mother for
    potential implantation in her womb.
11. No Biblical justification is currently possible for the freez-
    ing of embryos.
12. No Biblical justification is possible for surrogate mothers.

13. The kinsman-redeemer and the levirate are Biblical provisions for the continuation of a family and its inheritance. Neither is applicable to modern reproductive methods.
14. Compassion and sensitivity should be shown to the infertile couple, but Biblical principles must not be abrogated by emotions.
15. *In vitro* fertilization cannot be prohibited by Biblical principle, but the procedure has many problems that make its moral foundation uncertain.
16. No Biblical justification is possible for artificial wombs, except possibly for purposes of therapy of the developing baby, but not as a substitute for the developmental "mold" that takes place in the womb.

Notes and References

1. E. G. Postma, *The Banner* (February 11, 1977), p. 9.

2. Some latitude must be given here. Without question, some fertilized eggs are so severely abnormal in appearance that they are not viable. These could be discarded, but we must insist that all fertilized eggs that have any chance for survival be deposited into the woman.

3. Quotes and notes in this section are from Walter C. Kaiser, Jr., *Toward Old Testament Ethics* (Grand Rapids, Michigan: Zondervan Publishing House, 1983), pp. 190-192.

4. *Ibid.*, p. 192.

5. Archbishop of Canterbury's Commission (to study artificial insemination, 1945), quoted in Norman Anderson, *Issues of Life and Death* (Downers Grove, IL: InterVarsity Press, 1974), pp. 49-50.

CHAPTER 9

"World Overpopulation" and Birth Control

"So God blessed Noah and his sons, and said to them: 'Be fruitful and multiply, and fill the earth. And the fear of you and the dread of you shall be on every beast of the earth, on every bird of the air, on all that move on the earth, and on all the fish of the sea. They are given into your hand. Every moving thing that lives shall be food for you. I have given you all things, even as the green herbs. But you shall not eat flesh with its life, that is, its blood. Surely for your lifeblood I will demand a reckoning; from the hand of every beast I will require it, and from the hand of man. From the hand of every man's brother I will require the life of man.

> *'Whoever sheds man's blood,*
> *By man his blood shall be shed;*
> *For in the image of God*
> *He made man.*
> *And as for you, be fruitful and multiply;*
> *Bring forth abundantly in the earth*
> *And multiply in it'" (Genesis 9:1-7).*

For the second time early in the Bible, God repeats what He had said earlier about mankind's responsibility to procreate:

"Be fruitful and multiply; fill the earth and subdue it; have dominion over the fish of the sea, over the birds of the air, and over every living thing that moves on the earth" (Genesis 1:28).

Many people (both Christians and non-Christians) believe that mankind has obeyed God fully regarding this command. That is, the earth is saturated with people, having recently passed five billion and rapidly heading toward six billion. Loud cries can be heard that the world is dangerously overpopulated. The birth rate must be slowed or "spaceship earth" is doomed to die by the sheer numbers of people "aboard" it.

Since Thomas Malthus made his prediction in the 18th century, social planners have worried and warned that the earth's population will outstrip its resources, causing many to die of starvation. As evidence, these "prophets" point to famines around the world where millions die of hunger. Generally, medical professionals agree with this analysis and have pushed both birth control and abortion to limit population growth.

Are these "experts" correct? Are people really starving because the earth's population is outstripping its resources to produce sufficient food?

Indeed, these experts are wrong! As with all God's commandments, we have not been fully obedient, and the command to be fruitful and multiply is no exception.

A Medical Concern?

Some may wonder why population concerns appear in a book on medical ethics. Is this not a problem for social planners? The answer is "Yes" *and* "No." Yes, the earth's population is a problem for social planners *who have the proper presuppositions.* "No," physicians and other medical professionals must be concerned as well, because *we are the ones called to implement the ideas of the social planners.* We are the ones who prescribe the contraceptives and perform the abortions. The consequences of these acts are considerable, so we must understand the Biblical ethics on this issue.

The Cause of Famines

India can be viewed as an example to understand famines. For most of the 20th century, most people in India have been in

poverty with insufficient resources to feed its people. Within
the last few decades, however, *India has become an exporter of
food*, donating 100,000 tons of wheat to the people of famine-
ravaged Ethiopia in 1985. What happened to cause these
changes? Primarily, the changes were new agricultural methods and incentives for farmers to produce.

Even before these changes, however, a problem was evident as cows wandered among starving people. The cows were
sacred and could not be killed for food *for religious reasons*.

The famine in Ethiopia has received considerable focus in
the media in recent years, but rarely have the true problems
been presented.[1] Traditionally, Ethiopian farmers had stored
food from productive years for the non-productive years that
eventually came. In addition, they worked their own farms.
The present government, however, changed the entire system.
Those who tried to store food were accused of hoarding and
often punished. Farmers were relocated into collectives and
associations. Those who tried to transport food were accused
of "exploitation."

Then, when the drought hit, years of poor productivity,
lack of storage and transportation produced a severe shortage of
food and massive starvation. Even when other countries came
to the rescue with massive amounts of food, the government
was known to confiscate many of the shipments. Those that
were not confiscated often did not reach people in need because
of an inadequate transportation and distribution system.

More recently, Somalia was targeted for relief by the
United States and the United Nations. While many nations and
relief organizations had sent food for the starving of this war-
torn country, bands of marauding soldiers prevented its distribution to their own people!

Thus, the greatest factor in food production (or lack of
production) is national and cultural. Or in more accurate
terms, it is a religious phenomenon. The daily attitudes and
actions of a people determine its food production far more than
the weather or any other factor. The lack of a diligent work
ethic and tangible rewards will lock a culture into perpetual
starvation.

With this conclusion, I am not saying that famines never

occur as a result of severe weather. Indeed, they do. What must be understood, however, is that famines are far more often caused by how people of a region believe and behave culturally and religiously than the weather. And -- proper storage of food prepares a people for years of disaster. (Are *you* prepared? See Proverbs 6:6-11; 10:4-5; 20:4.)

Actually, the earth can support many times its current population. Colin Clark estimates that it could sustain 35 billion people on the "overconsumptive" American diet and 100 billion on the "adequate" Japanese diet.[2] Further, every person on earth could be housed in the state of Texas in a one-story, single-family home on an average sized American family's lot![3]

Thus, the facts are clear that we have not fulfilled God's Creation Mandate to be "fruitful and multiply." The call to limit population growth is the call of the religion of man. Its means of implementation, abortion, mirrors the evil nature of this call.

The Christian and "Birth Control"

For sure, the concept of the two-child family of the population planners has been believed by Christians as well as non-Christians. Just examine Christian families that you know. How many have limited themselves to two children? Fortunately, however, more Christians now seem to be having larger families. And the Bible is clear that God intended larger families.

First, God has never revoked the command, "Be fruitful and multiply; fill the earth...." Second, children are always called "blessings" in the Bible.

> *"Behold, children are a heritage from the Lord,*
> *The fruit of the womb is His reward.*
> *Like arrows in the hand of a warrior,*
> *So are the children of one's youth.*
> *Happy is the man who has his quiver full of them;*
> *They shall not be ashamed,*
> *But shall speak with their enemies in the gate"*
> *(Psalm 127:3-5).*

> *"Blessed shall be the fruit of your body, the pro-duce of your ground and the increase of your herds, the increase of your cattle and the offspring of your flocks"* *(Deuteronomy 28:4).*

> *"And Eli would bless Elkanah and his wife, and say, 'The Lord give you descendants from this woman for the loan [her first son, Samuel] that was lent to the Lord'* .... *And the Lord visited Hannah, so that she conceived and bore three sons and two daughters"* *(I Samuel 2:20-21).*

Of course, children are not the only blessings, but never does God speak of procreation in a negative manner. There is always the expectation of increase.

Third, Christians have overlooked the family as the primary mode of evangelism. A great movement today is to reach those outside of the church and in foreign missions. God's cove-nants, however, were always with a person and his "seed" (Genesis 9:9; 17:7; 35:12). This covenant is restated in the New Testament.

> *"For the promise is to* you and your children, *and to all who are afar off, as many as the Lord our God will call"* *(Acts 2:39).*

Also, children who receive the "nurture and admonition of the Lord" (Ephesians 6:4) in their formative years can be more effective to carry out the work of God's Kingdom. Those of us who did not receive this training realize how difficult it is to re-train our thinking and behavior.

The fastest growing religion in the world is Islam, primari-ly because of their large families -- an average of five children. Meanwhile, Christians are having two or three.

Fourth, the concept of "birth control" grew out of the eugenics movement earlier in the 20th century. Margaret Sanger and others were active to limit the procreation of those who were "mentally retarded, mentally ill, and socially inferi-or." This concern included the notion that children prevented the "good life," that is the freedom and finances to pursue one's pleasures. Both concepts grew out of the humanistic philosophy that man could "control" his universe. "Birth control" was consistent with their overall philosophy.

Euphemisms reveal a link between birth control and these attitudes, even among Christians. We speak of "the fear of pregnancy." A child that is not "planned" is an "unwanted child" and an "accident." Every woman has the "right" to avoid pregnancy. We use the factory term, "reproduction," instead of the traditional Christian concept of "procreation." It is to the shame of pro-life Christians that such expressions are part of our vocabulary. To be consistent with our position, we must work towards substituting language that reflects God's blessing in children and that all are planned by Him for His eternal purposes.

Ultimately, the motivation of birth control leads to abortion because it is the "fail-safe" and "back-up" for unplanned pregnancies. A contraceptive may be used, but when it fails, abortion is available to "solve the problem." Thus, *abortion is linked to and is the final "solution" to birth control.*

How Many Children?

The question that always arises in this context is, "How many children should a couple have?" The Creation mandate to "be fruitful and multiply" was given to husbands and wives. Thus, they decide the number of children that they will have. Until "the pill," accurate planning was quite limited, because birth control measures were not fully reliable. Now, the pill allows major control over the number and timing of children.

Such control, however, is still limited both morally and medically. We will review the moral difficulties of pills and other birth control means next. Medically, complications of certain birth control methods (below) and the problems of infertility (Chapter 8) are still unpredictable. More than ever, however, most families can have as many, or more likely, as few children as they desire. In their choosing the number of children that they want, they must consider certain facts.

First of all, God says "be fruitful and multiply." The uses

of "multiply" in the Old Testament indicate large numbers
(e.g., Exodus 1:7, 32:13; Job 29:18; Ezekiel 11:6). So, one's
first thought should be of "many" children. This thought is
confirmed by Psalm 127:5 (above). What man goes to hunt or
to war with only 1 or 2 arrows in his quiver? Of course, the
language is poetic, so this thought should not be taken too literally. Nevertheless, there is clearly the implication of "several"
children.

Perhaps, some demographic information sheds more light.
In Western society, approximately two children are needed per
family *to maintain the current population.* This number is
higher in Third World countries, where infant and child mortality is higher. So, one could conclude that at a minimum, Christians should average three children per family to continue to
multiply, following God's original mandate to "multiply."

We must not be too dogmatic about this number. The Bible
does not say, "Thou shalt have three or more children." Every
family should consider what God did mean by this mandate
relative to their family size. However, one cannot get away
from the general impression that He intended large families!

There are limiting circumstances. Temporary postponement may be necessary to finish college or graduate training.
Immediately successive pregnancies might be a hardship for
women with medical problems, so pregnancies could be spaced
over several years.

Poverty is a possible reason, especially temporary situations
such as the loss of a job or unexpected, large expenses. Generally, however, the costs of raising children are severely overes-
timated. Such figures usually consider the best of everything,
whereas large families are often quite ingenious in their ability
to provide sufficiently for every member of the family. Children can even work their way through college with little or no
expense to the parents.

Any family that uses a small income as a reason to limit
family size should be quite sure of their reasoning and motives.
Too often, they are primarily concerned to give every child the
"best" of everything. This approach, however, contributes to
the child's becoming an adult with unrealistic expectations. A
good example of large families who strived within their means,

yet often acquired great wealth through discipline, are the American-Chinese. While they came to the United States to take low paying and menial jobs, many have amassed considerable wealth and provided professional education for their children *in spite of their large families.*

Severe genetic deformities may cause a couple to choose not to have children. They should, however, consider the degree of severity and, most importantly, the incidence. Some genetic problems are almost certain and others are very unlikely to occur. Age (over 35 or 40) *per se,* however, does not qualify as a sufficient reason not to have children. There is an increasing risk of complications in pregnancy and birth defects with increasing age, but the occurrence is relatively infrequent and usually overstated for women who are otherwise healthy.

Voluntary childlessness for most other reasons is questionable. Any couple who chooses not to have children when they are physically able to do so should reevaluate their position in view of what God has said in His Word about children being a blessing to a marriage and to His Church.

The Morality of Birth Control Measures

With all that has been said, Christians should approach the concept of "birth control" with considerably less apprehension than unbelievers who go to any lengths to avoid pregnancy, including the murder of their unborn child. For Christians, no pregnancy is "unplanned." Ultimately, God plans them all (Psalm 139:16)! And -- He always provides for His own. Far and away, this principle exceeds the importance of what follows here. Christians should never plan anything without their considering that God may superintend with His own agenda (James 4:13-17). Birth control is no exception.

Birth Control Pills. This method is the only one that is 100 percent effective and virtually 100 percent reversible.[4] There are, however, three moral considerations for their use. 1) These pills do not always prevent ovulation. A strong contingent of pro-life people stand against the pill for this reason. The problem, of course, is the possibility that conception may occur, if ovulation occurs. With the conditions of the womb altered, the embryo fails to implant and is lost. If this process did occur, then there would be no doubt that birth control pills are immoral. It is certain, however, that such conception is very, very unlikely, if it occurs at all.

Consider these statistics. The likelihood of ovulation when a woman is on the pill is one in twenty-five. The likelihood of conception in women of child-bearing age without contraceptives is 10 percent. Thus, the possibility of conception based upon these two factors is one in 250 menstrual cycles. With the other changes in the reproductive organs caused by the pills, however, few if any sperm will actually reach the egg where it can be fertilized. We cannot say definitely that fertilization will never occur, but the likelihood is infinitesimal. Thus, I do not think that birth control pills can be opposed for this reason. (I have written a more detailed argument elsewhere. I will be glad to provide a copy to any reader who writes to me at the address on the cover of this book.)

2) Birth control pills have serious side effects. These include liver disease, high blood pressure, strokes, heart attacks and blood clots to the lungs. The frequency of these, however, is extremely rare. Further, the data is not clear whether there is any risk at all in women who do not smoke, are under 35 years of age, and who use the lower dose pills. In favor of the pills are their possible protection against fibrocystic breast disease, ovarian cysts, ovarian cancer, iron-deficiency anemia, pelvic inflammatory disease, ectopic pregnancy, rheumatoid arthritis and endometrial cancer. These benefits seem to cancel the risks and thus preclude the risk of physical harm as a moral prohibition against the use of these pills.

3) Birth control pills interfere with normal physiology. By definition, medicine is concerned with the treatment of disease and injury. (To some extent it is concerned with the prevention of disease, but space will not permit us to discuss that issue here.) These pills, however, disrupt *normal physiology*, even though, there seems to be little, if any, harm done (above). It seems incongruent that medicine should interfere in this way. Although this reason lacks a sufficient base to prohibit birth control pills, it should give pause for a woman to consider what changes the pills are causing in her body. Other forms of birth

control are adequate and effective when used correctly and cause much less disturbance of normal physiology.

Abortifacients. These medications or devices cause an inflammation of the womb that prevents a fertilized egg from becoming implanted. Thus, the embryo is lost without the woman ever knowing that she was pregnant, because she will not miss her next menstrual period. These methods include all intra-uterine devices (IUDs), the "mini" pill, progestin injections given every three months, the "morning-after" pill, and probably the new five-year hormone implants. Little needs to be said about abortifacients except to condemn them all. They destroy the life that begins with conception.

Other Methods. The remaining methods of birth control are the condom, spermicides, cervical caps, diaphragms, withdrawal (coitus interruptus), breast feeding, and the rhythm method. These are lumped together because there is little to preclude their use either morally or medically. They are less effective than birth control pills, but are sufficiently effective to avoid immediately successive pregnancies and to limit family size. Obviously, there are advantages and disadvantages, but we are primarily concerned with their morality. Individual preferences should be discussed with a physician.

Birth Control and the Single Woman

I find many pro-life physicians to be inconsistent on this issue. They stand strongly and actively against abortion but have few or no reservations about prescribing birth control measures for single women. They reason that the prevention of an unwanted pregnancy will prevent its being aborted. Their practice, however, is clearly wrong and unethical.

First, a decision to prescribe birth control to unmarried women is not the "lesser of two evils." Pregnancy is not an inevitable result of sexual immorality. Further, we may not *"do evil that good may come" (Romans 3:8)*. That is, the end does not justify the means. God never places any Christian in a situation where sin is unavoidable (I Corinthians 10:13). The physician is right to be concerned about the possibility of an abortion, but pregnancy is not the immediate problem. *Sexual immorality is.* God calls us to act morally in the present, not in some potential, hypothetical, future situation.

Second, the prohibition of both abortion and sexual immorality is included in the Ten Commandments. It is inconceivable that one Commandment can be violated *to prevent the possible violation of another.* Sexual immorality is destructive of the family, the foundation of both the church and the state. It is destructive of the individual. Some believe, as I do, that nothing affects the core of one's being as severely as sexual sin. The feelings of guilt and the impact upon one's spirit are almost overwhelming. Such results are as anti-life as abortion is.

Some physicians justify their actions with their telling these patients that they do not agree with their plans, but to prevent pregnancy they will give them the pills anyway. Such an explanation belies that physician's belief in the value of marriage. In effect, he says, "I value marriage and the sexual morality therein, but not enough to resist your request." He has not ministered to that patient, but denied his belief with his action.

Third, this practice separates a serious sin from its consequence. One deterrent to sin is a fear of its consequences. Agreed, most single women who are denied birth control will only go to another physician to obtain it. Nevertheless, the "blessing" of the physician as a person and as a member of the medical profession has been given to her immorality when he writes her prescription. In fact, *the physician is a proactive accomplice to the sin of fornication.*

Fourth, the physician may just prevent one or more women from initial or further involvement in sexual immorality. Agreed, the likelihood is small. Still, the woman may not have already engaged in sexual sins, and the unwillingness of the physician may be the influence for her not to do so.

Fifth, abortion demonstrates that what is permissible soon becomes acceptable and may even become required. For example, some medical training programs will not accept applicants who are opposed to abortion, and many will have similar difficulty with applicants who will not prescribe birth control for any woman who asks.

This demand, however, is backfiring. Programs that require their residents to do abortions are not being filled! In many situations, there are more applicants who are either pro-life or are concerned about being known as an abortionist in their community. They will not come to the training program if abortions are required of them.

Sixth, the physician is an accomplice to all the physical and psychological consequences of sexual immorality. Over 20 diseases are now considered to be sexually transmitted. We have previously discussed that many of these cause infertility, and a few (e.g., hepatitis B and AIDS) are killers!

The issue becomes clear if we make an analogy between the prescription of birth control and abortion. "I do not believe in abortion, but I will perform one for you because you can easily go to someone else to have it done -- because I may have an opportunity to minister or witness to you at a later time -- because I may be able to prevent a worse complication from occurring later -- because the consequences of abortion are not detrimental to yourself or to society." Presented in this way, the person who is opposed to abortion must also be opposed to birth control for single women, to be consistent.

Four situations should be distinguished from the above arguments. 1) Birth control pills are sometimes used to control irregular and heavy menstrual bleeding, usually in teenagers. 2) They are prescribed 2-3 months before marriage to enhance their effectiveness after marriage. 3) They may be used to control painful menstrual periods in women of all ages. 4) The same or similar hormones may be used in different dosages and combinations for other medical problems, but in doses that are not effective for birth control.

What About Sterilization?

Sterilization is the most definitive step that a couple can take as a birth control measure. Modern procedures are more than 99 percent effective. (Some may be surprised that they are not 100 percent effective.) They are tubal ligation for women (the tubes through which the sperm travel to fertilize the egg are cut and tied off) and vasectomy for men (the tubes that carry sperm from the testicles to the prostate gland, where they are stored until ejaculation, are cut and tied off). These procedures, however, today can be reversed. Such reversal has a success rate of 70-80 percent.

The question with which we are most concerned here is the morality of sterilization. Is it an option for Christians? Yes, there does seem a point at which one of these procedures could be chosen. The couple, however, must consider the gravity of their decision. Again, our emphasis here is a positive attitude (followed by changed behavior) toward larger families, moving away from the negative response ingrained in our culture by the birth- and population-control movement. Thus, after a couple has seriously considered their response to "be fruitful and multiply" and has had several children, they might choose this option.

Although complications from either procedure are uncommon, they do occur. A vasectomy is considered minor surgery, but a tubal ligation is major surgery, because the abdominal cavity must be entered where the oviducts are located. Thus, more serious complications occur with the latter. The exact procedure and its complications should be discussed with the physician who is to do the surgery. Moral considerations should be discussed with the couple's church leaders, and decisions justified according to a study of God's Word.

CHAPTER SUMMARY

1. God's command "to be fruitful and multiply and fill the earth" is still in effect.
2. Famines are not caused by overpopulation but reflect the culture and beliefs of the culture in which famine occurs.
3. The prosperity of a country is not related to its degree of crowding or the size of its population. Examples are Japan, Holland, Singapore, and Taiwan.
4. The earth is capable of producing food for a population that far exceeds current numbers.
5. Children are a blessing of God and an integral part of His plan for His people.
6. The family continues to be the primary mode of evangelism and training for the next generation.

7. Birth and population control, eugenics, abortion, genocide, and mandatory sterilization reflect the same humanistic philosophy that seeks total control of the environment and of people.
8. Christians must develop a positive attitude and vocabulary that reflects God's blessings through their children.
9. Under "normal" circumstances, three children seems to be a minimum for Christian families. Limiting factors include poverty, genetic deformities, and temporary postponement.
10. Birth control pills interfere with normal physiology and may be an immoral method for this reason.
11. All other forms of birth control are less effective, but are more clearly moral and are adequate for spacing pregnancies.
12. The condemnation of all abortifacients is consistent with the Biblical pro-life position.
13. The prescription of any method of birth control to an unmarried woman except for specific medical reasons is to be severely condemned and is incompatible with a Biblical position.
14. Sterilization may be a choice for some Christians *after* they have seriously considered their role in the Creation Mandate.

Notes and References

1. Chilton, David, "Planned Famine in Ethiopia," *Biblical Economics Today*, 8 (Fall 1985), pp. 1-4.

2. Colin Clark, *Population and Land Use* (New York: St. Martin's, 1977), page number not given, quoted in Hilgers, Thomas, *et al.*, *New Perspectives on Human Abortion* (Frederick, Maryland: University Publications of America), p. 455.

3. Editorial quoting Harold C. Christensen in *The Augusta Chronicle* (January 13, 1986), Section A, p. 4.

4. I am making two assumptions here. First, my statement is limited to *combination* (not sequential) pills with at least 30 micrograms of estrogen. There are many birth control pills with varying amounts of estrogen and progesterone on the market today. Second, the woman takes her pills *every day*, at the same time of day.

CHAPTER 10

"No Admittance, Healing in Progress"

"Yet I considered it necessary to send to you Epaphroditus, my brother, fellow worker, and fellow soldier, but your messenger and the one who ministered to my need; since he was longing for you all, and was distressed because you had heard that he was sick. For indeed he was sick almost unto death; but God had mercy on him, and not only on him but on me also, lest I should have sorrow upon sorrow. Therefore I sent him the more eagerly, that when you see him again you may rejoice, and I may be less sorrowful. Receive him therefore in the Lord with all gladness, and hold such men in esteem; because for the work of Christ he came close to death, not regarding his life, to supply what was lacking in your service toward me" (Philippians 2:25-30).

This is a strange passage! Paul the Apostle, Paul the miracle-worker, and Paul the healer seems to have made no attempt to heal a brother who was precious to him and to many other believers. Why?

Paul had healed on several other occasions. In Lystra, he healed *"a cripple from his mother's womb, who had never walked" (Acts 14:8-9).* In Troas, he brought back to life a young man named Eutychus, who had been killed in a fall from a third-story window (Acts 20:9-12). In another incident, he prevented the deadly effect of a snake bite upon himself (Acts 28:1-6). Furthermore, in Ephesus through Paul, God worked numerous miraculous healings that are not actually named in the text (Acts 19:11-12).

146

So, it seems that either Paul or someone with the gifts of healings (I Corinthians 12:9) would have healed Epaphroditus.

But Paul didn't, and neither did anyone else! Why? The only possible explanation is that Paul (and probably others with the gift of healings in the first century church) could not just heal at any time that they chose.

Miraculous healing has obvious relevance for the practice of medicine. If such healing is possible, the practice of medicine and surgery pale by comparison. The former is inexpensive, requires little physical work, and is momentarily and totally effective, whereas the latter is costly, often requires a great deal of work for many people, and recovery may be incomplete. Further, it is to God's glory that Christians fully experience those blessings that He has intended for them.

Today, many Christians, mostly charismatics and Pentecostals, not only believe in miraculous healing, but that it can be practiced on demand. And, they have many testimonies to authenticate such healing.

What is right? That is, what is *Biblical*?

God's Priorities Are Greater Than Miraculous Healing

You have seen in earlier chapters the degree to which lifestyle, both physical and spiritual, affects health and causes disease. Numerous Proverbs and other passages clearly state this expectation (e.g., Exodus 20:12; Psalm 90:10; Proverbs 3:2, 7-9, 15-16; 4:10, 22; 7:2; 11:19). Unfortunately, Christians are often guilty of these sinful (and unhealthy) practices.

Relative to miraculous healing, two principles seem clear. First, it is presumptuous to expect God to "bail out" the believer who has brought injury or disease on himself by sinful lifestyles. The Bible repeatedly warns that God's people will experience the consequences of their errant ways.

> *"Do not be deceived, God is not mocked; for whatever a man sows, that he will also reap. For he who sows to his flesh will of the flesh reap corruption, but he who sows to the Spirit will of the Spirit reap everlasting life"* *(Galatians 6:7-8).*

Second, if we are truly interested in health (the result of healing), then we will make it a regular part of our lives. We are especially guilty before God when we continually ignore his directions for our lives. In essence, we "want the gain without the pain." That approach to life is not God's plan. Repeatedly, He states that maturity and blessing (from which good health flows) come through diligence to follow His ways and not a slothful approach to life (Proverbs 6:6-11; 24:30-34).

Christians who would claim miraculous healing ought to proclaim more vigorously the lifestyle that is most consistent with the Biblical pattern of life and the modern knowledge of physical health. It seems, however, that miraculous healing receives greater emphasis than a healthy lifestyle, whereas the Bible gives greater emphasis to a healthy lifestyle rather than miraculous healing. This reversal is but one of several incongruities in Christians' approach to miraculous healing, but there are others.

Supernatural vs. Miraculous

An understanding of Biblical concepts will help to clarify what is and what is not miraculous healing. *Supernatural* and *miraculous* are often used as though they have the same meaning. However, God's more common and greater work is *supernatural*, not *miraculous*.

Christians, by contrast to atheistic evolutionists, believe in a supernatural universe. Simply, we believe in persons and places that cannot be "sensed." That is, these realities cannot be perceived with any of the human senses: sight, hearing, smell, taste, and touch. Furthermore, this supernatural world is the foundation of the world that we do sense. *"By faith we understand that the worlds were framed by the word of God, so that the things which are seen were not made of things which are visible" (Hebrews 11:3).*

Ultimately, then, all things are not grounded in the spiritual world, but in a Person who is *"upholding all things by the word of His power" (Hebrews 1:3). Supernatural,* then, names this working of God in human lives and in events in the universe that cannot be observed or discerned except for its effect. That is, the effect may be seen, but the cause is not. For example, Christians are being "transformed" into the image of Jesus Christ (II Corinthians 3:18). The cause is the Holy Spirit, Whose work is not detectable by human senses, but the effects (characteristics of holiness) are discerned in the believer over time.

A miracle is also God's "un-sensed" work with an observable effect, but it is not according to a predictable pattern. It is momentary and dramatic. For example, when a person becomes a Christian, he is "born again," but one cannot "sense" where this change *"comes from and where it goes" (John 3:8).* If the person is truly born again, however, a profound effect will be seen in his speech and behavior. Further, who will and who will not be "born again" is not predictable. Otherwise, we could save ourselves considerable time and effort in evangelism and preaching by going only to those who will respond. A miracle, then, is a category of the supernatural because God works by "un-sensed" methods as He does in the new birth.

Relative to health, the Biblical instruction that directs us in healthy practices is God's supernatural work. Miraculous healing is a special, unpredictable work. By far, the more common and the more important is God's supernatural effect on health, consistent with the Bible's emphasis.

Characteristics of Miraculous Healing

The Biblical criteria of miraculous healing are determined from observed characteristics of occurrences in the Bible. First, *such healing is instantaneous.* The effect is not seen days or weeks later, and neither is there a period of convalescence. The lame man that Peter healed immediately got up -- even leaped! (See Acts 3:1-10.)

Second, *the healing is complete, never partial.* This man did not require some time for him to develop the muscle strength to walk and leap, even though he would have had very few muscle fibers in his legs after a life of never using them. Also, he did not require the time and practice to regain his sense of balance -- a necessary skill to learn when one has not walked his entire life.

Third, *the availability of miraculous healing is clearly
unpredictable, even for those whom God used as His agents to
effect the miracles.* We began this chapter with one such
example. Paul would have healed Epaphroditus if he had been
able. In another instance, Paul instructed Timothy to "use a
little wine for your stomach's sake and for your frequent infirmities," instead of healing him (I Timothy 5:23). Miraculous
healing is not prevalent in the New Testament except for Jesus'
ministry and the early chapters of Acts. If it had been frequent,
and certainly if it had been as common as it is claimed to be
today, it would almost certainly have been mentioned in other
New Testament books.

Fourth, *the purpose of miraculous healings was to authenticate God's activity among men.* Jesus pointed to his "works"
as evidence for belief in Him (John 10:22-38). When John the
Baptist asked whether Jesus were the Christ, Jesus answered (to
John's messengers) with the evidence of His works (Matthew
11:1-19). The writer of Hebrews names these events as authentication of Jesus' ministry (Hebrews 2:4). Today, miraculous
healings are not needed to authenticate Jesus as Messiah and
Savior, because we have the infallible Word of God in the
Bible. Possibly, in Eastern countries and "regions beyond"
where the Bible is unknown, this authentication is needed even
today. (This author is doubtful, however.)

Fifth, *all recorded instances of healing in the Bible were
performed by a Prophet, Jesus, or an Apostle.* In other words,
healings were accomplished not only by the person having a
special power from God, *he was also recognized to have a
God-ordained, official position in Old Testament Israel or the
New Testament Church.* While some people today may claim
to have special powers of healing, their having an official office
recognized by a substantial segment of the Church of Jesus
Christ is doubtful. This lack virtually discredits their claim of
power to heal.

With these five characteristics, much that passes for miraculous healing today is not consistent with Biblical accounts.
Miraculous healing cannot be claimed if it is not both instantaneous and complete, yet many accounts today have taken place
over a period of time and the person is much improved, but not

completely healed. The claim by some healers to heal at special services or at any other time "on demand" reveals that they have powers that exceeded those of the Apostles, a most unlikely, even presumptuous claim!

Gifts of Healings

Listed with other gifts is the category of gifts of healings (I Corinthians 12:9). It is the only place this gift is mentioned in the New Testament. Curiously, it is plural (*gifts* of healings) rather than singular (*gift* of healing).

What then can we say about this verse? It implies, but does not necessarily mean, that Christians other than the Apostles were able to heal. These gifts could have been limited to the Apostles, since the Biblical record is explicit only concerning their acts of healing.

Whether other persons historically have had these gifts is unclear. Within this century, however, where reliable evidence is more certain because it is more substantial and recent, the evidence is against the possession of any gifts of healings. Many healers who have been closely examined and their "patients" questioned have been found to be frauds.[1] That these gifts are not present today is certain.

Do Miracles Occur Today?

Most likely they do. The objective evidence, however, is at least that they are rare and that most miracles that are claimed to be such are not miracles. Two factors that make miraculous healing a difficult area to discern are the subjective experience of illness and the objective evidence of healing.

Psychosomatic Illness. Health involves a great deal of subjectivity, that is, a personal interpretation of how one feels and other bodily symptoms. In psychosomatic illness, the patient has symptoms that do not have any detectable cause in his body. These symptoms may be mild, such as a slight headache, or they may be severe, such as complete paralysis of one or both arms or legs. What may not be understood about this phenomenon is that these people are convinced that they have a physical illness or limitation. (I am not saying that there are not some people who intentionally fake their illnesses, but they fall into the category of malingerers, not psychosomatics.) In fact, it is often difficult to convince them that they do not have something physical.

What happens when a person with psychosomatic illness goes to a faith healer or healing service or has hands laid on him? The result is likely to be dramatic, especially if he really believes in the healer's powers. Psychosomatic symptoms can affect virtually any part of the body and any disease complex. Thus, these persons can claim to have had any disease cured. Quite often they have made the diagnosis themselves or the diagnosis is made by the healer himself. The fact that they may have seen one or more physicians may further substantiate their claims.

Patient Understanding. I remember when I discovered this remarkable phenomenon. When I began to care for patients following medical school and internship, I would make notes in the chart to help me remember what I had told the patient and what I was thinking at the time. I quickly discovered that patients had selective hearing. For example, I might mention that cancer was a remote possibility, but the patient heard me say that he actually had cancer! Now, I will not deny that my ability to explain medical terms in words and concepts that the patient could understand may have been deficient. Nevertheless, the striking difference between what I understood and what they heard was clearly different.

What would happen if a patient with this remote possibility of cancer who believed that he *had* cancer went to a miracle healer or service and was healed! He (and certainly the healer) would claim to have been healed of cancer! Further, since he had seen a physician, he could claim that the medical profession had failed to heal him.

Placebo Effect. A placebo is a drug or other treatment given to a patient for its subjective effect. The treatment is known by the physician not to have any therapeutic value itself. The classic example is a "sugar pill" with nothing else in it.

What is remarkable is that it works! The effect is so consistent and strong that medical research is sometimes considered invalid unless a placebo is administered to one group of patients along with another group who receives the actual medication. Not uncommonly, the placebo group does as well, and sometimes better, than those who receive the medication.[2] Further, the placebo can actually cause physiologic ("real") changes! For example, blood pressure can be lowered, intestinal ulcers healed, and migraines relieved. (Of course, these "real" effects are mediated through the patient's mind, an additional demonstration of the unity of the body and the spirit of man.)

A dramatic example of placebo occurred prior to today's "heart-bypass" surgery. A procedure was designed to transfer an artery from the chest wall and implant it into the muscle of the heart to improve blood flow, previously impeded by atherosclerosis. When tried, the operation proved to be a remarkable success as it improved patients' symptoms and even objective tests.

Then, someone had the audacity to suggest that sham surgery should be performed to determine whether these improvements were due to this placebo effect. At first surgeons were quite reluctant. They were concerned with the ethics of denying an "effective" procedure to patients who needed it.

Eventually, however, the research was carried out. Those who had the sham surgery did as well as those who had the real thing! Afterwards, the procedure was abandoned. (One wonders if the same result might occur today with heart-bypass surgery, but how irreverent of me to suggest it!)

How the placebo effect can cause healing, then, should be apparent. Not only may patients with psychosomatic illness be "cured," but patients with real illnesses may be cured by this placebo effect. (See my discussion of faith, below.)

Self-Limited Disease and the Progression of Disease. Commonly noted among physicians is that 80 percent of all problems that patients present to physicians are self-limited. That is, their problems will get better regardless of what the physician does. (Sometimes, they get better *in spite of* what the physician does!) Mostly, these are minor ailments, such as colds, headaches, bruises, strains, etc. Sometimes, however, serious problems may resolve themselves. Spontaneous remission of widespread cancer, although rare, is well-documented.[3]

Furthermore, the progression of pre-cancerous tissue to full-blown cancers is not well-understood. In general, the progression of diseases is as unpredictable as the weather. Some are rapidly fatal, while other serious, life-threatening diseases go into remission and even disappear entirely.

What might happen if a person whose disease is undergoing remission or resolution simultaneously has a miraculous healing experience? The healer or the rite used gets a powerful witness, especially if the patient has been treated unsuccessfully by a physician.

Thus, psychosomatic illness, patient understanding, placebo effect, self-limited disease, and the naturally erratic course of diseases contribute to the claims of miraculous healing. Personally, I believe that they represent almost all, if not all such claims. Even so, it may be possible to document true miraculous healing. We now consider that possibility.

Objective Evidence Required

With the above conditions so difficult to unravel, it would seem reasonable to ask for objective documentation before miraculous healing is claimed. We find the description of such evidence for some Biblical miracles. They did not have the "sophisticated" means that we have today, but they were nonetheless objective. Everyone could see the "withered" hand that was "restored as whole as the other" (Luke 6:10). One blind man was known to be "blind from his birth" (John 9:1). Our previous example of the lame man healed by Peter was "lame from his mother's womb" (Acts 3:2). Lazarus' resurrection was four days after his death, a period of time that virtually eliminates the possibility that he was buried alive (John 11:39).

Certainly, all instances of miraculous healing in the Bible do not have such documentation. For example, the healing of the paralytic implies that his problem may have been partially or entirely psychosomatic (Matthew 9:1-8). That is, Jesus focused on the forgiveness of the man's sins more than his paralysis (v. 2). The same implication could be made of His initial words to the lame man at the Pool of Bethesda, "Do you *want* to be made well?" and His later admonition, "See, you have been made well. *Sin* no more, lest a worse thing come upon you" (John 5:6, 14, emphasis added). The woman crippled by a "spirit" (Luke 13:11) would today be classified by most physicians as psychosomatic, although she may have been possessed by an evil spirit.

A full discussion of these passages is complex and therefore too lengthy for our analysis. I am only *suggesting* here that a non-physical illness is one possible interpretation of each of these passages. Thus, all Biblical texts on miraculous healing do not present objective evidence of illness.

However, any claim today for miraculous healing would seem to require objective evidence. A claim for healing based upon personal testimony of subjective symptoms and signs without objective evidence has really said nothing important. *Anyone at any time can make a claim that he was healed in this way.* On a statistical basis alone, *almost all of these claims will be false without objective evidence* (below). Do we have the right to credit God with a majority of false claims? Surely, it is irreverent and presumptuous to do so.

What objective evidence is necessary? It could be a variety of things. The healing of a crippled limb could have pictures or measurements of changes in length before and after. Cancers could have previous microscopic tissue samples. Broken bones should have x-rays before and after. Infections should have cultures or other tests that show the presence of the offending agent.

Eyewitnesses are less reliable, but approach objectivity according to their involvement with the situation. For example, they should not be emotionally involved. A family member is too close to be objective. Also, many, if not most, charismatic and Pentecostal healing takes place in meetings that are highly emotional. Preferably, the witness should be someone who is skeptical of the approach that is used.[4] Also, there should be more than one witness. Eyewitnesses, however, are not irrefutable. There are recorded instances in which whole crowds were deluded.

Finally, and without refutation for Bible believers, are the Biblical characteristics of healing: instantaneous, complete, unpredictable, and in a situation where authentication of God's activity among men is needed.

The application of *either* objective documentation *or* Biblical characteristics would eliminate the large majority of miraculous healings. Applied together, they could eliminate virtually all such claims. God is not glorified by "crediting" Him with fallacious "miracles."

One possibly miraculous healing supplied the title for this chapter. A woman was diagnosed to have cancer of her large intestine, and x-rays showed an "apple core" deformity of her large intestine.[5] For physicians, this deformity is almost irrefutable evidence for her diagnosis. I have not searched the medical literature, but supposedly, this finding has never been present without this lady's diagnosis. She did not have, however, a microscopic tissue sample that would have made the diagnosis and subsequent story irrefutable.

On the night prior to her surgery, she had a healing ceremony according to James 5:14-16. During this ceremony, a sign was hung on her hospital door that said, "No Admittance, Healing in Progress." At surgery the next morning, she was found to have no evidence of cancer anywhere, including examination of the inside of her entire large intestine. I will grant the virtual certainty of this case. (I would like to find one case that will fulfill all the above criteria. Perhaps, a reader will submit such a case to me, but I have not yet encountered one.)

For sure, I am not saying that God cannot heal today. *I am saying* that the case against miraculous healing is strong. I fully expect to find some irrefutable, objective evidence, eventually. Most likely, it will come from a missionary, because reported cases of healing seem to be more prevalent in "regions beyond" (the previous reach of the Gospel). Further, such locations are possible places where God would substantiate His existence or provide miraculous care for missionaries who have chosen severe circumstances in which to proclaim the Gospel.

Call for the Elders of the Church

"Is anyone among you sick? Let him call for the elders of the church, and let them pray over him,

> *anointing him with oil in the name of the Lord. And the prayer of faith will save the sick, and the Lord will raise him up. And if he has committed sins, he will be forgiven. Confess your trespasses to one another and pray for one another, that you may be healed. The effective, fervent prayer of a righteous man avails much. Elijah was a man with a nature like ours, and he prayed earnestly that it would not rain; and it did not rain on the land for three years and six months. And he prayed again, and the heaven gave rain, and the earth produced its fruit"* (James 5:14-18).

This passage is the most explicit reference to the activity of Christians and the church and healing in the Bible. Its message is simple and clear in the English translation. (In the Greek, these verses are more problematic, but I have dealt with some of these problems elsewhere.[6]) Here, I will call attention only to certain points.

First, *the sick person himself calls for the elders* (or church officers of other titles). The family does not call and neither does anyone else. The passage does not explicitly exclude anyone else from calling, but the specific instruction is to the patient himself. Possibly, his faith to call has something to do with the outcome. The text implies that the sick person is too weak to *go* to the elders, so they must be summoned. At least, the elders should not be called for minor complaints, such as a "cold," indigestion, or mild headaches.

Second, *the elders are the ones called for.* Jay Adams has interpreted this instruction to include care by physicians.[7] This reasoning is based upon "anoint" (*aleipho*) that some interpret to mean the medicinal application of oil. This interpretation is, however, carrying the meaning too far for these reasons.

1) The call is for the elders. Thus, the physician who cared for the patient would have to be an elder of the patient's church. Of course, a physician could function under the authority of an elder, but that elder would have to have the knowledge of a physician to agree or to disagree with the physician's treatment. The situation is indeed rare where this meaning could be applied.

2) The extension of the meaning from "anointing" relatively benign oils applied to the skin to life-threatening surgery and other modern treatments is a giant leap. Rarely, does such an obscure meaning of one word from one passage have such a broad and extensive interpretation. In earlier chapters, we have seen how such a blanket permission for physicians to practice medicine without restriction can be both morally and medically erroneous. No, the elders are to be called for, not the physicians. Further, the meaning of "anoint" can as easily be interpreted as a ceremonial anointing as it can a medicinal application.[8]

3) Instruction is given for the possibility that sin may be relevant to the patient's illness (v. 15). We have already seen that sin can be directly or indirectly associated with illness or injury. The Bible here underscores this point again. No patient can be managed at the level of his physical problem only.

Note the conditional nature of the instruction, "if he has committed sins." The verse allows for the presence *or* absence of sin in association with the patient's condition. Elders (including pastors, since pastors are also elders) should be trained to explore the patient's life in this regard. Of course, with a sick person, this interview should be conducted with the utmost sensitivity. *But, it should be conducted*, if we are to follow the instruction of this passage. That this practice is ignored indicates how far we have strayed from the Biblical norm.

Simply stated, this passage ought to be practiced more often. Its instructions, however, should be carried out literally. Further, the implication of the passage concerns serious illness. Otherwise, the elders could be overwhelmed with calls for colds and other minor illnesses. Since interpretations vary, each church should exegete this verse and teach their understanding to their members. As with many practices, this one will differ from church to church. It is difficult for me to see, however, how such a clearly stated passage can be so widely ignored.

Finally, does the application of this passage automatically convey healing in every case? No, it does not. Healing could not occur in every instance, because everyone dies eventually. Further, Biblical instructions usually do not have an automatic cause-effect sequence. (For example, the children of believers do not always become believers themselves, even though "the promise is to you and to your children," Acts 2:39.) Many positive results could still occur with the closer involvement of the church and its leaders in the care of the sick according to this passage, however, instead of leaving the work to professions that are consciously anti-God and immoral.

The Role of Faith in Healing

Faith is foundational to the Christian's relationship with God (Hebrews 11:6) and to his salvation (Ephesians 2:8). Faith and belief, as synonyms, are prevalent in the New Testament. A paradox today, however, is that so many Christians understand the importance of faith but they understand little of the Biblical concept of faith. That lack is present with miraculous healing. In some cases, its focus with sick people is nothing less than cruelty.

For example, some are approached in this way, "If you have enough faith, you can be healed." Thus, miraculous healing becomes dependent upon the sick person himself. This approach, however, is a wrong understanding of faith. Certainly, some verses seem to imply that faith is under the control of the individual believer (Matthew 17:20; 21:21). Actually, however, it is not. Quite simply, "faith is a gift of God" (Ephesians 2:8). To be sure, it does become a part of the person: "... *your* faith has made you well" (Mark 5:34; 10:52). To be sure, faith grows with sanctification. At any given moment, however, the degree of faith exercised is not under the control of the believer.

Here we get into some serious issues of doctrine (free will vs. predestination) that have been a major debate in the history of the Church. For brevity, however, we will have to skirt that issue. We will rely on the two verses already mentioned (Ephesians 2:8-9). Faith is the "gift of God, not of works, lest anyone should boast." Very simply, but clearly and definitively, *if man is able to generate faith on his own, he may "boast."* Such boasting is prohibited by Scripture both here and elsewhere. For example, Paul says, "Let him who boasts, boast in the Lord" (I Corinthians 1:31). On the one hand, faith is a gift. On the other hand, it is something not to be boasted about by the Christian. Both statements agree. Having faith does not reside within the ability of the Christian.

A cruel burden is placed upon the sick person when his healing is made conditional upon his degree of faith. If he is not healed, he bears the devastating reality of insufficient faith. *His continued illness is his own fault.* Conveniently, the person who taught this erroneous concept of faith is always right. His reasoning cannot be proven wrong *in the situation.* If the sick person gets better, even healed, then the concept is proven. If the sick person does not get better, it was because he did not have enough faith.

CHAPTER SUMMARY

1. A focus on miraculous healing sometimes ignores the more important role of a lifestyle that is physically and spiritually healthy.

2. God's usual pattern is to work through supernatural means, not through miracles. Christians should understand the difference in the two concepts.

3. Miraculous healing has specific Biblical characteristics. It is instantaneous and complete, but not normally God's means of dealing with people.

4. The purpose of miraculous healings was to authenticate God's activity among men, a purpose that is not needed today (except in some remote regions). It was manifested only by Prophets, Apostles, and Jesus Christ.

5. The gifts of healings have not been proven to be present in this century and have doubtfully been present since completion of the Canon (i.e., books of the Bible).

6. Subjective interpretations of illness complicate the claim for miraculous healing. These include psychosomatic illness, understanding by patients, and the placebo effect.

7. Certainly, almost all claims of miraculous healing are false for these subjective reasons.

8. The Bible presents irrefutable evidence for miraculous healing. Thus, modern Christians ought to have such

evidence or not make the claim, else they falsify God's witness in the world.

9. The sick ought to call for the elders of the church in cases of serious illness. The elders ought to inquire about the possible relationship of sin to the patient's illness.

10. The application of James 5:14-16 does not always result in healing.

11. Healing that is dependent upon the sick person's having "enough" faith is not a Biblical concept and a cruel burden to place upon him.

Recommended Reading

Norman Geisler. *Signs and Wonders*. Wheaton, Illinois: Tyndale House Publishers, Inc., 1988.

Notes and References

1. Norman Geisler, *Signs and Wonders* (Wheaton, Illinois: Tyndale House Publishers, Inc., 1988.)

2. H. Benson and D. P. McCallie, "Angina and the Placebo Effect," *New England Journal of Medicine*, 300 (June 21, 1979), pp. 1424-1429.

3. Tilden Everson and Warren Cole, *Spontaneous Regression of Cancer* (Philadelphia: Saunders, 1966).

4. Some who believe in "faith" healing today might complain that the presence of a skeptic would itself prevent healing. That complaint, however, is really asking far too much of the rational Christian. An omnipresent, omnipotent God, if He chose to heal through the faith of His people, is hardly going to be limited by skeptical observers. What about all the skeptical observers present in many instances of Jesus' healing?

5. Betty Farmer, "No Admittance, Healing in Progress," *Guideposts*, June 1982, pp. 11-14. I have also seen pictures of the "apple-core" lesions that appeared on x-ray.

6. Payne, *Biblical/Medical Ethics*, pp. 129-132.

7. Jay E. Adams, *Competent to Counsel* (Phillipsburg, New Jersey: Presbyterian and Reformed Publishing Co., 1971), pp. 107-108.

8. W. E. Vine, *Vine's Expository Dictionary of New Testament Words* (Old Tappan, New Jersey: Fleming H. Revell Company, 1966; 16th impression), pp. 58-59.

CHAPTER 11

Medicine and the Civil Government

"For rulers are not a terror to good works, but to evil. Do you want to be unafraid of the authority? Do what is good, and you will have praise from the same. For he is God's minister to you for good. But if you do evil, be afraid; for he does not bear the sword in vain; for he is God's minister, an avenger to execute wrath on him who practices evil" (Romans 13:3-4).

"Therefore submit yourselves to every ordinance of man for the Lord's sake, whether to the king as supreme, or to governors, as to those who are sent by him for the punishment of evildoers and for the praise of those who do good" (I Peter 2:13-14).

I have no delusions about the chance of the following changes to be made any time in the near future. What *should be* (as described) is so far from what *is* that the difference seems remote and unattainable. However, a destination is never arrived at without specific directions to get the traveler there. If the Church ever wakes up from its modern stupor, then this chapter and others can provide the road map for the limited role of the state in medicine.

(In this chapter, "state" will be used to denote civil government at all levels: federal, state, and local, unless otherwise designated. Biblical "government" is founded upon the individual, the family, and the church. When they do not function in society as they ought, the state moves into the vacuum with an increasing tyranny.)

Should Physicians Be Licensed by the State?

The Apostle Peter (above) states that the legitimate role of the state is the punishment of evil. Where then, do we find the modern system in which the state, as a licensing agent, determines who will and will not practice certain disciplines: medicine, psychology, sociology, teaching, hair dressing, etc.? Our focus is on medicine, but the critique applies to other areas of licensing as well.

Indeed, *I contend that the state does not have the Biblical right to govern the practice of medicine.* The state has the right to become involved in medicine only when there is reasonable evidence of criminal intent or breach of contract on the part of a practitioner.

That position causes all sorts of dilemmas. Who will pay the tremendous costs (greater than $50,000 per year per student and $120,000 per year of specialty training) of medical education? Who will prevent a plethora of semi-trained charlatans and quacks and protect the public from them? How will the general public know to whom to go for treatment of their problems?

To my knowledge, the 20th century is unique in its licensing of physicians. In the United States, licensing and formal requirements for medical education did not exist until the late 19th or early 20th century. In fact, the regulation of medicine in the United States is probably greater than anywhere in the world (even in socialist countries). For example, many drugs are used in other countries that are not "approved" for use in the United States. Also, tribal witch doctors practice their ways in many countries simultaneously with modern medical practices.

The rebuttal to my position is that such regulation guarantees competent physicians and a standard of excellence for medicine. The evidence, however, is that such a cause and effect does not exist. First, the effectiveness of modern medicine is seriously doubtful even when judged by its own standards. (See Chapter 3.) When Biblical morality is brought to bear on medical practices, modern medicine often promotes disease and death. As we have seen, birth control allows the

sexual promiscuity that has brought a plague of sexually transmitted diseases (even without AIDS). Abortion is considered
"sound medical practice," even as it kills the unborn child.

A devastating argument against state licensing has been
developed by Dr. Stanley J. Gross.[1] His book is devoted to the
question of state licensing with particular emphasis on psychology and the health professions. It cites numerous studies that
licensing fails to achieve the goal of either quality care or
"protecting" the public. Actually, *licensing prevents a higher
quality of medical care from being achieved.*

Second, the state is not able to recognize which health
professions are legitimate. A clear example is chiropractic.
This practice was begun in 1895 by an itinerant tradesman and
"magnetic healer" who manipulated the spine of a deaf man to
restore his hearing. With that dramatic cure, chiropractic made
its start as a profession, in spite of the fact that it is based upon
a theory that is illogical and without scientific foundation. In
the extensive study of human physiology over the last few
decades, nothing has been discovered that might substantiate
their theory that manipulation of the spine will affect disease
processes.

Yet, the practice is recognized as legitimate by the state
along with the orthodox practice of medicine. I am not opposed to freedom for chiropractors to practice their art. I
merely point out that state licensure operates on political rather
than empirical, scientific grounds.

Third, it is clear that increasing numbers of people are
convinced that they are better able to determine what is and is
not effective medicine than "orthodox" physicians licensed by
the state. Examples of this self-confidence include self-help
groups, the prosperous practices of "unorthodox" healers, religious groups who will not see a physician, and trips abroad
(especially to Mexico and Europe) for various treatments at
great expense.

Thus, the state's regulation of medicine to assure competence by its practitioners, to protect citizens from charlatans,
and to develop the science of medicine is already seriously
ineffective and even contributes to disease (unrestricted treatment of sexually transmitted diseases) and death (abortion).

This book began with the premise that medicine is inherently a religious endeavor, because it is far more subjective than many other "sciences," such as chemistry and physics. Medicine, because of its treatment of one dimension of man (the body), is directly influenced by religious beliefs. I contend that the legitimate authority for the practice of medicine for Christians is the church. James 5:14-16 clearly establishes this role. The direct care of the healthy and diseased body is the responsibility of the family and the church. We will explore their specific roles in the following chapters.

Good Medical Care Is What the State Says It Is

The practice of medicine, as we know it today, began in the early 1960s. Of course, the seeds were planted much earlier, but their fruition began about that time. This practice of medicine was a part of the welfare initiatives of the day. It was generally believed that the poor and elderly needed more accessible and better medical care. Unfortunately, it was also believed that the state had the responsibility to provide these needs. (See Chapter 4.) Thus, Medicare and Medicaid began. All but the staunchest conservatives were pleased, as those who were formerly without medical care streamed into the "system."

Physicians were pleased, as well. The state increased their third-party payments dramatically. They were now paid for the care that they had formerly had to discount. Patient loads increased. Needless to say, physicians' incomes increased. At first, the system, as an attempt to establish the "right" of medical care to all, was one with little accountability by either physician or patient. Abuses occurred on both sides. Patients wanted, even demanded, all that was available to them, and more. Physicians ordered more tests and did more procedures because they would now be paid for them. They usually charged the maximal allowable payment as well.

Costs of these programs far exceeded expectations, so the state began to pay only a percentage of the physicians' charges. This maneuver did not bother physicians, because they only charged more, so that the percentage given them equaled their "normal" charge. More recently, the state has said that it will pay only a certain amount, regardless of the physician's charge. Then the protests began!

Increasingly, the state has also said what the physicians can and cannot do. The physician must prescribe drugs from an approved list, or the state will not pay for them. The physician is limited in the number of times he can be paid for patient care visits and how often certain procedures can be done. Certain patients need more care than the allowed limit, but little flexibility is built into the system. Indeed, the system must be rigid, or physicians and patients would again use that flexibility to their own ends. Essentially, then, through the medical welfare system, the state increasingly determines what is and is not "good" medical care. The carrot to the physician has turned into the iron hand of state control.

The Alphabet Soup of Health Organizations

Pre-payment systems are also worrisome. These include HMOs (Health Maintenance Organizations), PPOs (Preferred Provider Organizations) and other acronyms. These programs are attempts to control the costs of medical care for individuals and families. Members (or their employer sponsors) pay a predetermined amount, and this amount (within certain guidelines) is all they are ever supposed to pay.

The same problems, however, occur here as they do in state payment programs. The system determines how the physician treats the patient. He must choose from a list of approved drugs. He can do procedures only under certain guidelines. He can refer patients only to those specialists who are "approved," regardless of their competence. To admit patients, he must often call someone (who may not even be a physician) several hundred miles away to determine whether a procedure, a treatment, or hospitalization will be paid for under the patient's plan.

Worse, many programs use an incentive formula for physicians. Referrals to specialists, certain tests, and other patient costs come out of a lump sum that they receive at the end of the year. Thus, physicians are caught in a moral dilemma. They will have to weigh the patient's welfare against a decrease in their own incomes. Thus, physicians are encumbered with numerous restrictions. Not only must they evaluate and treat the patient, they must do so within the "system."

In a real sense, these "alphabets" have descended from state programs. We have seen how state money through immoral taxation and fiat money have distorted realistic expectations in medicine (Chapter 4). Costs have become prohibitive for all but the very rich. No system can survive without requiring responsibilities that balance "rights." The state and our society have pretended that medical care can be given regardless of moral requisites. The financial chaos within medicine is proof that it cannot.

Morality, Medicine, and Health

Probably the greatest step the state can take to increase the health of the American people is to re-enact laws that reflect traditional (Biblical) morality. For example, divorce is far too easy, because the laws are not consistent with Biblical criteria for divorce. An entire book has been written that demonstrates that married people are considerably more healthy than those who are single, widowed or divorced (of any age) in almost any disease category.[2]

Observance of the Sabbath rest is likely to cause an increase in health. Many people's lives consist of seven-day work weeks, whether they are working at a job at a business or at home. Thus, they face considerably more stress than they would if they rested one day in seven.

The current problem with AIDS is a direct result of laws that permit not only tolerance of homosexuality, but actively promote it. Many states still have laws against homosexuality but now see them as antiquated. That is not to say that these laws are the best application of Biblical law to society against homosexuality. It *is* to say that our legal system did once oppose homosexuality and had punishments for its practice.

Other problems have been discussed elsewhere. Abortion is a fatal "disease" that is protected by law. Its prohibition would not only give life to the unborn, it would likely decrease child abuse and enhance the structure of the family altogether. Sexually transmitted diseases are more prevalent because they can be treated at public expense without censure of, or payment by, the one infected. The legal prescription of birth control pills for unmarried women causes disruption of families and promotes the spread of STDs also.

The Training of Physicians

The training of physicians is another dramatic change that would have to occur if the state reversed its control of medicine. Currently, future physicians enter medical school after 3-4 years of college. They go four more years to medical school and an additional 3-7 years for specialty (called "residency") training. Medical students pay tuition, but it is only a small fraction of the yearly cost of their education (see the beginning of this chapter). Residents are paid a salary (currently in the $20,000+ range). They treat a large number of patients because their level of expertise is higher than that of a medical student. Still, the difference between their salary and educational expenses minus their generated income is considerable. From where would such funding come with the state out of medicine?

Likely, medical schools would not exist. A few might be found, if they were heavily endowed or that had sufficient patient revenues, student fees, and other income. Mostly, the training of physicians would be by apprenticeship, as it had been for most of history. This pattern raises several questions.

Who will certify that physicians are competent? First, the church has a role that we will discuss in the next chapter. Basically, it will approve, perhaps ordain, the spiritual qualifications of physicians and their general competence in medical matters. Second, more responsibility will be placed upon the patient as a "consumer." He will have to do more "homework" to find a trustworthy physician. Christians will have the additional sanction by the church of certain physicians.

Probably the biggest loser in this transformation will be the physician and his income. He will no longer be subsidized by the state. True competition will occur among physicians, causing their charges to decline. Throughout history, physicians have rarely been the affluent members of society that they are today. Insurance payments will be fewer and more consistent with an "appropriate" charge.

(I do not relish a lower income any more than anyone else, but I must value the reconstruction of medicine along Biblical guidelines more than my own advantage.)

There Is a Legitimate Role of the State in Medical Care!

The state should make provision for illnesses and injuries that occur to soldiers, policemen, and other state employees during wartime and in their action against criminals. Currently, such provision far exceeds these activities. In the armed forces, families, as well as soldiers, are given complete medical coverage. In some situations this "benefit" may be appropriate: where the soldier and his family are stationed in a remote or foreign place, if the soldier's pay is insufficient for him to pay for such coverage, and possibly other reasons. Generally, however, these families should pay for their own care as other families do. (There are problems with military pay, but in general they are beyond medical concerns.)

My experience in the Veterans Administration system is that the majority of its work has to do with medical care that is not related to military service (the supposed reason for its existence). In fact a large portion of their work concerns the complications of cigarette smoking and alcoholism. It is a system that especially places the costs of sinful behaviors on the rest of society through taxation.

Thus, the role of the state in the provision of medical care should be quite limited -- even miniscule -- compared to the gargantuan role that it plays today.

Public Health and the State

The state's role in public health needs to be radically changed, as well. Its only legitimate role seems to be standards for sanitation and public health. Requirements in the Torah include specific instructions for sanitation (Deuteronomy 23:9-

14). Thus, the general principle that sanitation is necessary for the health of one's own family and that of others is clear. Further, sanitation has to do with the prevention and control of evil. Without authoritative intervention, the disposal of refuse would pose a serious threat to others, as it did before the spread of infections was understood. With modern industry, this role extends to the regulation of industry in the disposal of its wastes.

Another legitimate role for the state is the control and quarantine of infection (Leviticus 13-14). This authority allows the state to limit the spread of infectious diseases. As individuals and families, we have neither the authority nor the ability to keep our neighbors from activities that would expose us to certain infections. Yet, the irresponsibility and sometimes evil intent of neighbors directly and indirectly threaten us in the same way. In this "small" world of modern travel, as far as infections are concerned, all peoples become our neighbors. Thus, within and between nations, the state exercises the necessary authority to control infectious diseases.

The state's authority, however, is limited in this area as it is elsewhere. For example, the state currently has a massive immunization program, but is it legitimate? Without the state, what would become of this role? The state should retain its role to track epidemiological patterns of disease that are spread by casual contact.

It is not necessary, however, for the state to administer the immunizations. Responsibility would fall to individuals, families, churches, and other organizations rather than the state. Since public education is not a legitimate role of the state, either, immunizations in schools would be the responsibility of each school. Businesses would require proof of immunization. Churches in their pastoral oversight would require or recommend appropriate immunization. Those who chose not to be immunized merely face the consequences of their own negligence. Responsible people would get themselves immunized and require the same of those over whom they had responsibility and control.

The state certainly does not have a role in the regulation and treatment of sexually transmitted diseases. These are transmitted almost entirely by sexual activity and primarily by *immoral* sexual activity. These diseases would virtually disappear in one generation (except for those unfortunate babies who contracted them from their mothers) with the Biblical restriction of sexual activity to marriage. Thus, contact tracing of sexually transmitted diseases is not a legitimate role for the state.

The role that the state has played in public health education has definitely been detrimental to our society. We have seen throughout this book that health is directly related to moral behavior. Yet, public health education today is taught without morals. Actually, it is taught with *perverse* morals, because that is the end result of any approach without a standard. Thus, for sure, the state has no role in health education. Parents and churches are responsible.

Surely, you say, we cannot do without state research. But, we can! As medicine cannot be practiced without morals, neither can research. Many breakthroughs already come through commercial institutions and private foundations. With fewer controls and the competitive atmosphere of the free market, research might even move faster than it currently does. Many large studies could not be done, but the experience of individual physicians and scientists would eventually achieve the same results. Some momentum might be lost in the initial changeover, but the advantages overall and long term would outweigh the short-term disadvantages.

The loss of the role of the state in drug control seems dangerous, but only if patients and physicians fail their own responsibility. Without "FDA (Food and Drug Administration) approval," the physician would have to rely more upon his profession's knowledge and experience with a drug. The patient would have to be more careful in his selection of physicians and drugs. All drugs would be non-prescription, but patients would not want to take potentially dangerous drugs without physician advice. If they did, they would face the consequences (whether good or bad) of their decision. The situation would not be as bad as it seems. Most countries of the world today do not have drug control. The United States did not until this century.

A pattern seems clear in the removal of the state from most

medical and related roles: responsibility falls more directly to individuals, families, churches and other groups. Indeed, are these groups not where responsibility should lie, Biblically? Almost everything that the state does is more costly, less efficient, and harmful. Practically, then, the role of the state in medical care should be removed except for those roles that are Biblical. These are the treatment of illnesses and injuries that are directly a result of legitimate civil or military service, and control (including quarantine) of certain infectious diseases.

CHAPTER SUMMARY

1. The state does not have the Biblical right to govern the practice of medicine.
2. Consistent with this principle, the state should not be involved in the licensing of physicians.
3. The licensing of physicians and other professionals has not "protected" the public and has actually promoted disease and death.
4. Under the present system, medical care is strictly limited to those standards that are acceptable to the state.
5. Pre-payment systems (HMOs, PPOs, etc.) have their own inherent problems.
6. Health is promoted most effectively by a society that is moral and governed by Biblical standards and law.
7. Under a Biblical system, medical schools would be rare. Physicians would be trained primarily in apprenticeships.
8. The state has a legitimate role to provide medical care for diseases and injuries acquired in the "line of duty" by policemen, firemen, and other civil servants.
9. The state has a legitimate role in sanitation and refuse disposal and in the control of infectious diseases.
10. Without current state control, more responsibility for personal health must be assumed by individuals, families, and churches.

Notes and References

1. Stanley J. Gross, *Of Foxes and Henhouses* (Westport, Connecticut: Quorum Books, 1984).

2. James J. Lynch, *The Broken Heart: The Medical Consequences of Loneliness* (New York: Basic Books, 1977).

CHAPTER 12

The Church and the Practice of Medicine

*"Do you not know that your body is the temple of
the Holy Spirit who is in you, whom you have from
God, and you are not your own? For you were bought
at a price; therefore glorify God in your body and in
your spirit, which are God's" (I Corinthians 6:19-20).*

In these verses, the body is identified with the Holy of
Holies, the most inner sanctuary of the Temple. It is here that
the Holy Spirit dwells in believers. Thus, the body is not just a
physical entity that will die and decay. As such, the role of
physicians who care for the bodies of believers must be taken
quite seriously, certainly more seriously than the present situation in which physicians either participate in or approve of the
murder of unborn children and are accepting of euthanasia.

Am I My Brother's (Medical) Keeper?

The cost of medical insurance for pastors and their families
has become a major cost in many local churches and denominations. Some of the insurance plans that provided coverage for
their families have gone bankrupt. There is great concern
about providing such coverage, but evidently the concern is not
sufficiently great to examine the Bible to determine what ought
to be done! In this area, as in many others, the Church follows
the methods of the world. Is it any wonder that such insurance
plans are bankrupt?

In Chapter 4, we examined reasons that current medical
payment systems do not work. From that review and other
subjects covered by this book, churches and denominations

174

ought to reexamine their medical insurance plans and begin to design new ones.

Such redesign will not be easy and may not be legally possible. Every state has its own insurance regulations, and these are often tied to federal funds and programs. All this regulation may prevent the legal implementation of any insurance plan that is truly Biblically based. It seems to me, however, that the Church has no alternative but to consider alternatives.

While Christian ought always to obey the laws of the state, there are times when those laws restrict the fulfillment of God's commandments that we love and care for each other. Some creative and innovative thinking needs to be brought to bear on this crisis within the Church.

First, and most important, God has called His Church and His people *not* to be *"...conformed to this world, but be transformed by the renewing of your (their) mind..." (Romans 12:2).* Inherent in every Christian's mind ought to be the question that when some area of life fails, "How did I (we) go wrong Biblically?" Medical insurance is failing miserably and catastrophically.

And, that failure is the second motivation for insurance reform. *The current medical insurance system will not work.* That statement ought to be repeated. *The current medical system will not work!* Am I getting through? The current system is forcing reform, so why not go to the Bible to find a design for its reformation?

Certain principles may be derived from Chapter 4. 1) The state has no role in medical care other public health and the care of those with diseases or injuries from service to the state (policemen, firemen, soldiers, etc.). 2) The church must expand its role in charitable medical care (see below). 3) There is no universal right to medical care or medical insurance. 4) Personal responsibility for individual and family health must be built into any payment system. 5) "Mental health" coverage must be excluded or rigidly limited.

The *Christian Brotherhood Newsletter* is one example of Biblical creativity applied to medical coverage under the present system (Chapter 4). Its costs are far below those of standard insurance programs for similar coverage. (Read their brochure carefully, however, as there are differences that you need to be aware of.) *Without state regulation*, a program could be designed that would cost much less.

Alas, that may not be possible in today's world, but are we not building for the future, as well? To have already examined today's failures and made Biblical reforms would make us ready to implement a plan when the opportunity comes!

Claiming the Counseling Prerogative of Churches

Chapter 5 examined the fallacies of modern psychology and psychiatry, as well as the failure of the Church to provide counseling for its own. The correction of this severe departure from Biblical oversight of Christians should be a priority of reform by churches as a demand from Christ Himself. But, further, this correction would impact greatly on medical costs.

Insurance for "mental health" is one of the fastest growing segments of medical insurance, because it is virtually open-ended. Almost any negative emotion or irresponsible behavior can be labeled a mental disorder and even coded for insurance coverage. No doubt you have received brochures from "Christian" centers who state that they can "treat" you at little or no cost to you because of insurance coverage. *These people are charlatans defaming the name of Christ!*

Sin is sin and ought to repented of through individual conviction or dealt with under the discipline of the local church (see below). *These problems are rarely medical, and it is a lie and misrepresentation to call them such.* I will leave the door cracked for the "gray areas" mentioned in Chapter 5, but these are so few (when Biblically and scientifically examined) as to be negligible for this discussion.

The Practice of James 5:13-16

Many churches and pastors will not agree with my interpretation of this passage in Chapter 10. Nevertheless, I call all church boards, sessions, and church leaders to study this text and have an official plan for its implementation. *This passage is the most comprehensive passage in the New Testament governing the management of the sick by the church.* It ought to have an official and active status in every church.

Further, James 5:13-16 provides for ...

Relationships Between Physicians, Pastors, and Churches

The inherent religious content about which this entire book has been written requires a closer relationship between the practice of medicine and the church.

Certainly, James 5 requires some investigation by the elders into many illnesses. "If he has committed sins" and "confess your sins to one another" clearly shows that sin may be a problem in some Christians' illnesses. The implication is that elders must develop sensitive "antennas" to know when such investigation ought to occur. To many readers, such activity may appear to be a throwback to church inquisitions. However, the past errors of the Church must not limit truly Biblical roles for churches today.

The Apostle Paul calls for "gentleness" and carefulness in such situations (Galatians 6:1-5). Indeed, elders should have manifested such characteristics *before they were ordained* (or installed). That is, elders ought to be Christians in whom church members would have every confidence to deal Biblically with such situations. Otherwise, they should never have been elected and ordained (or installed) in the first place!

Beyond this oversight of the elders, local churches and denominations must seek closer relationships with physicians. From the other side, Christians in medicine (or those going into medicine) must become more knowledgeable about the relationship between illness and sin.

I am not sure what this relationship ought to be on each side. I will make some suggestions for starters. All pastors will need physician advisers, because their pastoral role includes frequent attention and care for the ill. Further, pastors and elders may need to talk with trusted physicians *before* they investigate what sins may be related to a particular illness (i.e., a James 5 situation).

I see a "partnership" for physicians and pastors to help each other. Most Christian physicians need more Biblical and theological understanding. Most pastors need more medical understanding. *Each can teach the other.* Perhaps, every pastor should have the discipleship of at least one physician as one goal for his pastorate. Seminaries may need to involve physicians more in the training of young pastors.

Perhaps more students planning to be physicians should plan some time for seminary or other formal theological training, especially in the early transition from the current medical system to one more consistent with Biblical principles. The physician would have to be trained to recognize sinful behaviors that contribute to disease, as well as be able to teach healthy patterns of spiritual life. Such patterns include a disciplined and scheduled life, Sabbath rest, and regular Bible study.

Certainly, pastors and physicians must seek to break the identification of every personal and social problem as one that can be solved medically. Secular psychology has a stranglehold on the Church, and the medicalization of problems is not far behind. Pastors and other church leaders must recognize and challenge this invasion of their territory.

Availability of Biblical Counseling

Integral to the relationship of medicine and the spiritual life is a Biblical understanding of "mental illness" (Chapter 5). Dr. Jay Adams and other nouthetic counselors have provided needed materials and training to accomplish this task. Dr. Adams' most thorough books are *The Christian Counselor's Manual*, *Competent to Counsel*, and *More Than Redemption* (Zondervan Publishing Company). In addition, he has numerous other books for counselors and handouts for counselees. Others who agree with his Biblical approach have written other materials, as well. No other counselor (including psychologists and psychiatrists) have come close to the Biblical thoroughness or practicality of his approach.

A physician cannot practice medicine that is Biblically oriented unless Biblical counseling is available for his patients. The physician himself does not have to provide the counseling. He may not have the time nor the spiritual gifts to do so.

Nevertheless, such counseling should be available through a local church or counseling center. Where these are not available, he may work with a local church to train the pastor to counsel or bring in another pastor who is trained in Biblical counseling.

This education needs to be carried into Christian schools, as well. Too often the physical education program is little different from that of public schools. Students need to learn and participate in programs that emphasize aerobic conditioning rather than competitive sports, in which some children are unable to participate and which will not be useful for the remainder of their lives. Christian schools should be leading the attack on the abysmal physical condition of American children.

Backup to the Family

In the provision of needs, the church is to be a backup to its families. While the family is commanded to provide for its own (I Timothy 5:8), there are times when its members are not able to do so, despite their best intentions. At those times, the church must be prepared and willing to get them "back on their feet." That provision includes medical care within the limits set by all that has been discussed in this book.

One area not mentioned elsewhere concerns hospitalization of a family member. Trips to the hospital and long stays with sick patients can be whelming for many families. A good diaconate program ought to have individuals "on call" who can help in these situations.

Another area for consideration is whether a church should require that its members have medical insurance. In its backup role, the church could find itself responsible for tens or hundreds of thousands of dollars in medical bills. It ought not to place itself at such risk. The church, however, ought to have the names of one or more insurance companies that could provide this coverage for its members. Medical coverage with high deductibles is one approach that should work in this situation.

Preaching and Teaching

The "risk factors" that have been discussed in several places in this book must be preached and taught in the local church. The verses that introduced this chapter teach that the physical body is the temple of the Holy Spirit, the Holy of Holies. As Christians, we do not worship the body, but give it a great deal of care and conditioning. This education of Christians would reinforce the structured insurance program (above) and vice-versa.

Mission Boards

The humanism of medicine has penetrated our mission boards. Christians who are well-qualified to go the mission field have been turned down for medical reasons. In other instances, they have been sent home from the mission field for reasons of health. In both instances the missionaries themselves were quite willing to take the risks associated with their conditions, but the mission boards were not. Would the Apostle Paul's thorn in his flesh (whatever it was) have disqualified him from the hardship of his missionary journeys?

Some mission boards routinely use psychiatrists to screen those going to the mission field and those returning home. It seems that calling and spiritual qualifications are no longer sufficient for Christians to be missionaries. They have to meet some sort of mental health criteria.

The shift in thinking here is not subtle. These mission boards may not have shifted entirely from the spiritual model to the medical model, but they have certainly given considerable credence to the latter. One wonders whether Hudson Taylor with his pigtail or Adoniram Judson with his eccentric ways (and frail health) would be considered to be "in touch with reality" and allowed to go to the mission field today.

Church Discipline

Perhaps the most neglected responsibility of the church today is discipline of its members. Whenever this subject is mentioned, people almost immediately think of "witch hunts," both literally and figuratively. A church, however, cannot be spiritually healthy without the disciplining of its members. Therefore, it cannot be physically healthy either, since we have seen repeatedly that spiritual health is an absolute prerequisite to physical health.

Church discipline is much more than punishment of members. In fact, this aspect ought to be a only small part of church discipline. The greater part should be a church's expectation of its members to learn sound doctrine and a Biblical worldview. Usually, one simply transfers one's membership from one church to another. Beyond that, there are no specific expectations of members. They do not even have to attend worship services or make contributions!

This "easy believism" hardly reflects the rigorous training that the Bible teaches (Hebrews 5:12-6:2). Every school from the university to the elementary school to the secretarial college has a structured curriculum. Few churches, however, have a structured curriculum for their members. No wonder the army of Christ is virtually impotent. It is never expected to start school, much less to finish!

Behavior is infectious. We tend to be like those we are around. When Christians see other members of their church being lazy, they tend to follow. The same can work in the opposite direction. When the general activity of a church is vigorous, it will be a stimulus for all its members.

If the activity of a member does not meet minimal expectations or is involved in open sin (and the spiritual age of each member should be considered), then censure and even excommunication should occur. Let us remember, however, that the goal of discipline is never excommunication. The goal is restoration (II Corinthians 2:3-11). If, however, the person under censure is not repentant, then excommunication must be carried out according to God's instructions (Matthew 18:15-20). Also, the whole procedure is one in which those who exercise discipline are careful to consider themselves vulnerable as well (Galatians 6:1-5).

Again, Jay Adams has provided the church with a valuable resource concerning church discipline.[1]

Should the Church Have Chronic Care Institutions?

In the next chapter, I will place the family at the center of medical concerns. The question arises here, however, whether the church should develop nursing homes to provide for those situations where the care of the patient seems more complicated or difficult than the family can handle. Nursing homes may be an unavoidable solution, but the better route seems to be a well-trained and well-staffed team to help the family in the home.

First, nursing homes are expensive. Few families can afford such care. Second, nursing homes are just that. They provide nursing care. Although patients with different problems require differing types of nursing care, the same patient generally requires the same hourly and daily routines. These routines can be learned by members of a family. If something occurs that they do not know how to handle, then, they could call on someone from the backup team. Third, the home is far more healthy for a patient than an institution. We will review those advantages in the next chapter.

The backup role of the church must be reemphasized here. Many patients will be difficult to handle at home. The church needs a well-organized team to communicate with families who are caring for chronically ill members and provide assistance as necessary. Families can easily become whelmed with the burden of such a patient.

Medical Clinics

The role of the church in welfare includes medical care. Jesus' parable of the Good Samaritan was an example of medical welfare. As with other welfare programs, such help should not be blind. Medical care must be carefully administered. First, the church should not attempt to treat the supposed medical causes of immorality. To do so is to condone sexual promiscuity and the other self-destructive behaviors presented elsewhere. It should not be involved in birth control except in those instances where there are clear medical reasons to avoid pregnancy.

Second, the cost can quickly escalate. The primary goal of

the church to evangelize and teach/train its members must not be lessened by a medical program. Numerous cost reductions have been mentioned in this book and can be determined from an analysis of medical research. A effective medical care program can be instituted without great cost.

One distinct opportunity that the church has in this role is Biblical counseling. Every primary care physician knows that 25-50 percent of his practice has to do with the direct or indirect effects of spiritual (in medical parlance, "psychological") problems. These almost always involve conflicts within families, economic stresses, or problems in the work place. Truly Biblical counseling can offer permanent and complete "cures" for these "medical" problems. In the experience of many physicians, however, the patient is more interested in a physical explanation than a spiritual one. Thus, the fruits of such a ministry may be few, but for those who are willing to hear, the answers are more complete and certain than anything that the medical profession has to offer.

In this medical role, the church may have to provide institutional care. As the state withdraws its provision of medical care (and it will, if only because of economic limitations), an increasing number of people will be unable to afford care. Some will need long-term nursing care without family to care for them.

Nursing homes, staffed with caring Christians, are a real opportunity to serve these with great physical need and greater spiritual needs. Such a ministry will be extremely difficult and expensive, given the rigorous requirements of the state for nursing homes today. Some Christians will need to experiment in this area as a model for the remainder of the church to see what is feasible. Current costs make such institutions seem impossible for the ministry of a church, but some creativity can likely overcome the cost factor.

CHAPTER SUMMARY

1. The church must develop Biblical plans for meeting medical costs and not follow the world's standards that are now bankrupt. Basic medical care is an uninsurable risk.

2. The church must re-establish itself as *the counseling resource* for Christians and not continue to allow medical redefinition of sin as disease.
3. All local churches ought to have an official plan for the practice of James 5:13-16.
4. Pastors and other church leaders should develop a close working relationship with one or more physicians, especially with those who are open to Biblical teaching and the application of Biblical principles in medical situations.
5. The church is the backup resource for its families, including the provision of medical care.
6. Preaching and teaching should include the care of the body as the Temple of the Holy Spirit.
7. Mission boards have largely adopted the "medical model" for its missionaries.
8. A fully implemented program of church discipline would prevent many medical, as well as spiritual, problems.
9. The church ought to consider carefully its role in chronic-care institutions and medical clinics.

Notes and References

1. Jay E. Adams, *The Handbook of Church Discipline* (Grand Rapids, Michigan: Zondervan Publishing House, 1986).

CHAPTER 13

Health Starts With the Individual and Family

"Then Levi gave Him a great feast in his own house. And there were a great number of tax collectors and others who sat down with them. But their scribes and the Pharisees murmured against His disciples, saying, 'Why do You eat and drink with tax collectors and sinners?' And Jesus answered and said to them, 'Those who are well do not need a physician, but those who are sick. I have not come to call the righteous, but sinners, to repentance'" (Luke 5:29-32).

For our purposes, this passage contains two messages. First, those who consider themselves "well" (righteous) do not need a "physician" (Savior). Second, Jesus implies that often those who are "sick" (hardened sinners, i.e., scribes and the Pharisees) do not recognize their need for a physician (Savior).

While the emphasis of Jesus' teaching here concerns sin, the literal meaning of His statement has profound implications for health and medicine. *The truly righteous will not need a physician nearly as often as those who persist in their sin.* While I have already developed the relationship of sin and physical sickness in Chapter 1 and other places throughout this book, some specific applications may be made for the individual and family.

Spiritual Health of Individuals and Families

Family physicians have long known that both children and adults of distressed families have many more injuries and instances of sickness than do healthy, stable families. Indeed, this observation has been well-documented in the medical and social literature. A recent report summarized many of these studies and showed the striking contrast between the medical needs of distressed and healthy families.[1] *Spiritual healing of families is the most effective way to promote health and reduce their medical needs.* (One will wait a long time, however, before this fact is trumpeted in the news or by sociologists and liberal politicians as a solution to the health-care crisis.)

Unfortunately, Christian families are not as healthy as they should be, either. To take action to promote their own spiritual health is the most direct route to their avoiding the need for a physician.

I am not aware of formal studies of Christian families, so what follows is from my own medical practice, counseling experience, the observations of others, and the families that I have observed in the churches of which I have been a member.

First, a Sabbath rest is frequently not a rest at all. While the intent of Sabbath includes worship, it is also for rest (Exodus 20:8-11). Sunday is often a full schedule of services and meetings. Then, Christians often participate in recreational activities actively (such as, swimming, boating, skiing, and hunting) and passively (televised sports events). *Both worship and rest are thereby diminished or discounted altogether.*

While there are zealous Christians who promote aerobic exercise, nutrition, and unorthodox remedies, they often overlook the basic fundamentals of health: the basic fundamentals of the Christian life. The Sabbath is one of them.

Second, even Christian families have hectic and irregular schedules. While we are on the Sabbath theme, Sunday morning in Christian homes is often a panic scene with children to get dressed, lessons to learn or prepare, church responsibilities to meet, and breakfast to eat. Such is not exactly the right attitude for either worship or rest. A little planning and curbing of Saturday night activities would go a long way in helping to avoid this scene. Perhaps, a short personal or family devotional would even start the day off properly.

But, this Sunday scene is not too dissimilar from the rest of the week. Bedtimes are irregular, with meetings (often at church), homework, television shows, sports events, and other activities. The body and the mind cannot rest in an expected and comfortable cycle. Thus, the full benefit of sleep is not achieved either.

Third, broken relationships exist in Christian homes. There seem to be two reasons. 1) Just plain old sinful pride and self-centeredness is a great obstacle. 2) Christians often know what they should do but lack an understanding of how to put it into practice in actual situations.

Pride and self-centeredness must be dealt with before the throne of God. However, we return again to the teachings of Dr. Jay Adams for practical instruction. I have often cautioned people about reading him with the admonition, "After you read Dr. Adams, you will have no excuse, because you will know both *what you ought to do* and *how to do it.* You will no longer be able to claim any excuse of ignorance."

For example, Dr. Adams says that a lack of love in the home is the fault of the husband, not the wife.[2] We husbands will have difficulty dodging that missile! The reality of Biblical solutions in personal relationships within the family can be tested by the presence or absence of the words, "Will you forgive me?" "I am sorry" is not Biblical and does not require a response from the person injured. Biblical forgiveness requires both the one who asks and the one who grants. It results in powerful healing and strengthening of relationships.

These three areas are presented as examples to demonstrate that Christians ought to examine the beams in their own eyes before they try to cast aspersions on the pagans! *Spiritual health is the prerequisite to physical health.* Let's put the priority where it ought to be.

Making a Transition From Institutional Care

Medical care over the last several decades has shifted from its being primarily in the home or the physician's office to the hospital and nursing home. In this transition, much has been lost that needs to be regained. Further, the increasing costs of medical care in institutions may force a reversal of this movement. When this happens, Christians need to be ready both in attitude and preparation. The advantages of this change,

however, are likely to outweigh the disadvantages by a considerable margin.

Many patients who are now hospitalized (and especially
those who are in nursing homes) can be cared for at home. At
first, home care will seem a burden for many families, because
our modern "mobility" will be restricted. However, children
will learn firsthand the realities of chronic illness and basic
nursing skills (a forgotten art). The diaconate of a church will
have to get more involved in such care to provide where the
family is not able (I Timothy 5:3-16).

The Home Is a Healthy Place

First, everyone who has been a patient in a hospital knows
that hospitals are not a place to rest! Needles, pills, tests, noisy
instruments, and other interruptions continue almost twenty-
four hours each day. How much more comfortable are the
familiar surroundings of home, its conveniences, and quiet.
While the importance of rest in the healing process may not be
quantifiable, I have every confidence that it would be considerable. (At least that is what I desire when my illnesses arise.)
No doubt many complications in the hospital and other institutions are caused by a lack of rest and disruptions of other body
systems and defenses.

These problems are even more difficult for the elderly,
whose mental faculties may be compromised. Away from
familiar people and surroundings, they often become agitated
and combative. The patient may injure himself during these
times or the medical (drugs) or physical restraints used to
control the patient may cause serious injury. It is not uncommon that such agitation becomes a more serious problem than
the medical problem for which the patient was admitted. All
the while, this second problem could have been avoided if the
patient had been managed at home.

Second, more serious infections can be acquired in the
hospital than at home. The bacteria that cause these infections
have been exposed to the latest high-powered antibiotics and
have "learned" to resist them. This resistance can be very
difficult to treat. The infections acquired outside the hospital

are almost always easier to treat and are considerably less expensive. And, if a study were done, I believe that the number of infections would also be less.

Third, the conclusions are in for intensive and coronary care units. *They have not been found to be the life-savers that they were intended to be.* Several studies have shown that most "heart attacks" can be treated as well or better at home than in the hospital. Further, chronically ill (rather than acutely ill) patients occupy their beds.

Yet, the expenses of these units probably average $1500 or more a day! I don't think that many families would choose such treatment if they had to pay for it directly! Yet, when it costs us nothing directly, we say, "Do everything you can, Doctor!"

Fourth, inactivity can cause blood clots to accumulate in the legs, and they may break loose to travel to the lungs, where they can cause severe complications and even death. Other less common occurrences include getting the wrong medications and accidents in patient transfers from place to place.

Fifth, patients are over-medicated in hospitals. Laxatives, sleeping pills, tranquilizers, and analgesics are routine. Many of these are not really needed and may benefit the nursing staff more than the patient. Since *all drugs have harmful effects*, the more drugs a patient is on, the more likely untoward effects will occur. Further, these drugs often depress the senses and restrict people to their beds for longer periods of time than is necessary.

A growing movement along these lines is deliveries of babies at home and in birthing centers. Advocates point out that these births are safer than hospital births for women *who have no known risks of labor and delivery*. Apart from the medical aspects, these deliveries offer the exciting possibility of making births a family event. The husband and any children can participate in various ways to make the mother more comfortable in a setting that is not foreign or frightening for her.

Personally, I still have some reservations about this different approach, but am willing to consider the evidence. What is needed is a conference of Christian physicians to study the evidence for and against and make a recommendation for the Christian community.

Self-Help Books Are Needed

As we have seen, many medical problems are preventable or their onset may be delayed and/or diminished. Comprehensive instructions is this area need to be written by Christians. Some are already available, but most have significant omissions of certain problems. Others need to be written for children so that proper care of their bodies can be implemented at an early age. Basic instructional books on common remedies are needed.

When the state begins to withdraw various medical services by economic necessity, then the real family "doctors" (that is, mothers) will need to know how to handle basic problems. This situation will not be new. It has existed for most of history until the last 40 years in the United States and elsewhere in the West. Without the Food and Drug Administration, the array of drugs available to the lay person will be far greater than it is today. Reliable books on the uses of these medicines will surely be needed.

To avoid personal biases as far as possible (medical care will always be highly subjective), these books ought to be at least approved, if not developed, by churches. In addition, as we have seen, Biblical interpretation is fundamental to one's approach to medical problems. The church can play an invaluable role in the oversight and approval of such books.

Christian Physicians

(Note: What follows is brief. Appendix 2 gives a lengthy discussion on the personal and professional lives of physicians.)

Radical proposals have been made here! I do not claim to have all the answers. I do claim to a serious effort to be faithful to Biblical truth. If modern medicine is compared to its past, my proposals will not seem too far-fetched. Throughout history, medicine in most cultures was far less structured and comprehensive than it is today.

When we turn to the Bible, we do not find a mandate for Christians to seek the services of physicians. (See Appendix 1.) Indeed, all healing in the Bible is miraculous. Thus, we must seek principles consistent with Biblical truth that apply to the practice of medicine. Toward this end, the following proposals seem necessary.

Too many Christian physicians are dominated by their profession and their own self-interests. The starting point for them is to "practice what they preach." Certain activities are Biblically required of all Christians. Spouses and children must be given time for interaction, training, and problem-solving. There must be a systematic and regular approach to Bible study. There must be involvement in one's church, according to the spiritual gifts that are discerned by oneself and confirmed by others. There must be one's own program of physical health, especially exercise. All these activities take considerable time, but that time must be scheduled. The care of patients should not prevent these pursuits.

Christians who are entering medicine should seriously consider Bible school or seminary training prior to medical school. Too often, the years in medical school set behavioral patterns that continue for the remainder of one's life. The time demands are so great that Bible study, church activities, personal Bible study, and family life are set aside, never to be resumed. In addition, the thoroughly humanistic/ evolutionary approach in all medical schools must be discerned so that its impact is minimized.

Another possible time is immediately after one's first post-graduate year from medical school (formerly called "internship"). After this year one is able to be licensed to practice medicine. Thus, by working only a few hours a week in an emergency room, enough income can be made to support attendance at a Bible school or seminary, even with a family. Certainly, we need many more physicians in medicine with Biblical understanding to help us sort out the issues.

As in other areas, discerning Christians must take every opportunity to make an impact on our humanistic society. Physicians in academic centers should consider devoting their careers to the application of the Bible to medicine. Scholarly activities are expected in this setting, so why not advance the Kingdom as one advances one's career? This direction is not without risk, because such activities do not rank as high as such things as research and may even get one fired. I believe, however, as evidenced in my own case, that we can do far more than what we are doing now. Most often, we believe that the opportunities are not there because we have not tried. (In truth, the humanistic influence everywhere has become rampant because Christians have not done what they ought!)

Letters-to-the-editor are an easy way to make some impact. These are much easier to get published than regular articles. Often, editors are willing to publish a letter that differs from their position, where they will not publish anything of substantial length that they differ with. The *American Medical News* is subscribed to by over 300,000 physicians and publishes several letters each issue. A subscription to it for this reason alone is worth its cost, but it also keeps one up to date on many ethical issues. I have found it to be a valuable resource. I would subscribe directly, rather than join the American Medical Association to receive it as a member, since the AMA has ethical positions with which a Christian cannot agree, and its memberships costs are prohibitive.

The Christian Medical and Dental Society is another possibility, but it has leadership and theological problems. Its virtue is its republican form of government, so that it could be controlled by Biblically discerning Christians. The process, however, would take at least ten years, given its current organizational structure and election of officers. For the sake of unity, an attempt to turn it in the right direction seems the right approach. I have chosen that route, but the inertia that I have encountered is great. Others may want to try this route and make their own evaluation.

Two other physicians and I have started the *Journal of Biblical Ethics in Medicine*. It is addressed to a wider audience than just physicians, but its aim is to provide a forum for the exchange of Biblical principles that govern the practice of medicine. It has been well-received nationally and is beginning to receive international attention.

Also, in 1990, I started *Biblical Reflections on Modern*

Medicine, an informal newsletter that supplements the *Journal.* It is published six times a year. (See the back of this book for ordering information for both the *Journal* and *Reflections.*)

Re-evaluation of Medical Care

I am convinced that *everything* that physicians do must be subjected to close scrutiny. Nothing can be assumed to be "good medical practice." *Primum non nocere,* "First of all, do no harm," needs to re-gain dominance among physicians. In a hedonistic society such as ours, physicians are under great pressure to "do something" when a person is "dis-eased." Too often, the results are unnecessary tests, ineffective and/or harmful medications prescribed, and unnecessary surgery. Further, the manipulations or medications administered during this process may make the outcome far worse than when the problem was not even attended to medically.

Take the Ball and Run With It

There is much to consider and much to be done. The next several years will provide strong challenges for Christians in medicine, as well as for their patients. Churches will have to develop types of care with which they are not now familiar. The good news is that many of these changes will be positive for individuals, for the church, and for medical/health care in general. We must work and study to be prepared for these opportunities.

CHAPTER SUMMARY

1. The greatest effect on health or ill health occurs in the home.
2. Many Christian homes need to apply basic Biblical principles to make their homes more honoring to God and healthy to themselves.
3. In the next several years, a transition from institutional care to home care can be expected. This change will mostly be a positive one.

4. The home, as a place for treatment, has several advantages that will have a favorable impact on recovery.
5. Practical books on health care for families need to be written.
6. Christian physicians need to re-evaluate their approach to medicine in light of the Bible and coming changes in our health-care system.

Notes and References

1. Bryce J. Christensen, "Critically Ill: The Family and Health Care," *The Family in America* (May 1992). Published by The Rockford Institute, 934 North Main St., Rockford, IL 61103-7061.

2. Jay E. Adams, *Christian Living in the Home* (Phillipsburg, New Jersey: Presbyterian and Reformed Publishing Co., 1972), p. 100.

A Bible Study: Health, Healing, and Medicine

With the numerous books that have been written by Christians in modern times about medicine and medical ethics, I have seen no one examine *what the Bible actually says about medicine, physicians, healing, sickness, and patients.* The following is virtually a reprint from my first book, *Biblical/Medical Ethics.* My current book would be incomplete without these references to give a proper and complete Biblical perspective on medicine.

The focus is almost exclusively on the New Testament because: 1) it is generally more explicit than the Old Testament in its directions for Christian practice, and 2) many Old Testament principles of health fall under the ceremonial law, which no longer has direct application today.[1]

Since the selected words are used in New Testament contexts where the indicated healing may be spiritual, physical, both, or unidentified, those contexts which clearly reveal the healing to be of a physical nature are referenced more frequently than those that are less explicit.[2] I use "healing," "health," etc., only to refer to man's physical nature. For example, when Jesus healed (*hugaino*) the man with the withered hand and made it "like the other (hand)" - an explicit physical restoration occurred.

My primary goal is to derive any timeless principles from these words and contexts that might be applied to the relationship between Christians and their physicians.

"Physician" in the Old and New Testaments

The Greek word for "physician" (*iatros*) appears seven

times in the New Testament, six of which are used by Jesus. In Matthew 9:12, Mark 2:17, and Luke 5:32, He is speaking to scribes and Pharisees during a banquet in the home of Levi. These Jewish leaders have criticized His association with publicans and sinners. He responds, "It is not those who are healthy (*ischus*-Matthew, *hugies*-Mark and Luke) who need a physician, but those who are ill" (*kakos*). His statement might be used to indicate that those who are ill should see a physician, but Jesus is giving a spiritual message, because the next verse states that He came "to call the righteous, not sinners." Thus, the spiritual instruction of this context where "physician" is used gives no principle for the ethical relationship between a Christian and his physician.

In Mark 5:25 and Luke 8:43, the account of a woman with a "flow of blood" is presented. Over a twelve-year period, this woman had suffered at the hands of physicians, had spent all that she had, and had gotten worse. (An account that is not uncommon today!) She was hoping to be healed (*sozo*) and was cured (*iaomai*) by touching Jesus' garment. Then, Jesus pronounced her healed (*sozo*) and whole (*hugies*). In this context, *iatros* is used historically, not didactically, so there is no principle to be derived concerning the Christian's relationship to a physician.

In Luke 4:23 Jesus quotes a colloquial proverb, "Physician, heal (*therapeia*) yourself." John Calvin comments upon the context and the application:

> "A physician ought to begin with himself, and those immediately connected with him, before he exhibits his skill in healing others....(Christ) acted improperly (from their point of view) in paying no respect to his own country (Nazareth), while he renders cities of Galilee illustrious by his miracles."[3]

Since the saying is quoted by way of colloquial and contemporary analogy, the context does not allow for a principle to be established between physicians and their patients.

Finally, in Colossians 4:14 Paul calls Luke, the "beloved physician." Several passages in Acts (16:11-18, 20:5-16, 21:1-

19, and 27:1-28:16) use the first person plural pronoun, indicating Luke's travels with Paul. Further, Luke was probably with Paul when he died (II Timothy 4:11). No passage states whether Luke ever ministered to Paul as a physician. However, "it cannot well be regarded as an improbable or arbitrary assumption that at least one of the Apostle's objects in this visit to Philippi was to have the benefit of the beloved physician's advice for the state of his health."[4]

This likelihood is more certain when one considers that Paul was beaten, shipwrecked, imprisoned, and hungry (II Corinthians 6:4-5), and had a physical ailment which God had chosen not to heal (II Corinthians 12:7-10). However, this likely scenario is purely conjecture and cannot be extrapolated into a general principle. We can say that the Apostle Paul had a deeply personal relationship with Luke, and that Paul identified Luke with his profession.

In the Old Testament, "physician" appears four times. King Asa is chastised for seeking help from physicians rather than from the Lord (II Chronicles 16:12). Egyptian physicians embalmed Jacob (Genesis 50:2). Job calls his accusers "worthless physicians" (Job 13:4). Jeremiah calls for the spiritual healing of the wounds which have been produced by the sins of Israel (Jeremiah 8:22). These references are all historical and thus cannot be used as the basis for a principle for all believers.

In summary, the occurrences of the word "physician" in both the Old Testament and the New Testament do not allow for the derivation of an ethic for a Christian's relationship to physicians. It is worthwhile to note that there is neither an explicit command for any Israelite or believer to seek the services of physicians nor is there an explicit command not to do so.

(Note: An extensive reference to the physician and the value of his work does appear in the Apocrypha (Ecclesiasticus 38:1-15). Among Protestants, however, the Apocrypha is not included as Holy Scripture.)

Biblical Words Associated With Medical Care

Heal, Healing. *All instances of healing in the Old Testa-*

*ment and the New Testament are miraculous, with no recorded
healing from treatment by a physician!* However, there are
many uses of words that are associated with healing and health.

The following review shows that the Bible uses the word
healing to refer to the healing of the spirit as well as healing of
the body. In some instances, it is difficult, if not impossible, to
decide which is indicated by the context. Even today, however, physicians frequently cannot distinguish between the two,
since many patients have problems that are not clearly physical
or spiritual. It is erroneous, then, to conclude that all instances
of healing in the New Testament are spiritual. Many contexts
provide sufficient detail to leave no other conclusion except that
a true healing of physical disorder occurred. Interestingly, *only
Christ and His Apostles are recorded as having performed these
healings.*

Therapon. This word occurs forty-nine times in the New
Testament, thirty-eight times as a verb (*therapeuo*) that is translated "heal" in the KJV. All but three instances (Matthew 8:7,
17:18; John 5:10) refer to acts of generic healing (e.g. Matthew
4:23, 8:16; Mark 6:5; Luke 9:6; Acts 28:9). In Matthew
15:30, a variety of problems is listed: the lame, crippled,
blind, and dumb. Etiologies (causes) are not always specified,
but a demonic cause is identified in some contexts (Matthew
12:22; Luke 6:18, 8:2). The primary use of *therapon* and
therapeuo is to designate generic acts of healing, that is, the
text does not identify specifically whether the body or spirit was
healed. The word is sometimes applied to healing of problems
that are clearly demonic. In some passages, it is used explicitly
in reference to physical healing only.

Iaomai. This word has the same root as *iatros*. It contrasts with *therapon*, first, in its frequent use to refer to individuals with identifiable physical problems: paralysis (Matthew
8:8), hemorrhage (Mark 5:29), demonic fits (Luke 9:42), fever
(John 4:47), lameness (John 5:13; Acts 3:11), and dysentery
(Acts 28:8). Second, this word is explicitly used to identify
spiritual healing (Luke 4:18; Hebrew 12:13; I Peter 2:24). The
same quote from the Old Testament appears three times
(Matthew 13:15; John 12:40; Acts 28:27). Total New Testament occurrences are thirty-four, including the forms *iama* and

iasis. Twenty-four occurrences are clearly physical (including one demonic cause). Three are spiritual. Three are generic. Three (I Corinthians 12:9, 28, 30) designate gifts of healings. (See Chapter 10.)

Sozo. The primary use of this word, which occurs 111 times in the New Testament, denotes salvation (root of "soteriology," the study of salvation). In some instances, *sozo* means safety of the physical body from harm or death (e.g., Matthew 8:25, 14:30). Its use in other contexts often identifies a clearly physical problem, e.g., the woman with the flow of blood (Matthew 9:21, 22; Mark 5:28, 34; Luke 8:48, 50), blind Bartimaeus (Mark 10:52; Luke 18:42), the lepers (Luke 17:19), and the man lame from his mother's womb (Acts 4:9).

Diasozo. Derivations of this stem occur eight times. Two may refer to physical healing (Matthew 14:36; Luke 7:3), but the context does not explicitly identify a physical problem. It more commonly refers to being safely brought through some threatening circumstances (Acts 23:24, 28:1).

Hugies. From this root, comes the English word "hygiene," but Biblically, *hugies* may designate spiritual health (Luke 5:31, 15:27) or physical healing: the man with the withered hand (Matthew 12:13; Mark 3:5), the woman with the flow of blood (Mark 5:34), and a lame man (Acts 4:10). It is interesting that seven of twenty-six occurrences in the New Testament concern the paralyzed man at the Bethesda pool (John 5:4, 6, 9, 11, 14, 15, 7:23). The reason for its frequency in this context is uncertain. The context, "Do you wish to get well?," suggests a spiritual etiology, i.e., of the will to get well, but that conclusion could not be stated with absolute certainty. Other uses are to describe sound doctrine (I Timothy 1:10; Titus 1:9) and sound speech (Titus 2:8).

These five words have a primary contextual use to denote the miraculous healing of physical problems, yet there are distinctions among them. *Therapon, iaomai,* and *sozo* include healing in cases of demonic possession. *None are ever used of healing accomplished apart from God's miraculous intervention or have association with physical agents (i.e., medications) or physicians.*

If you examine a concordance, a dramatic decrease in the

frequency of the word "healing" occurs after the Gospels and Acts. This fact seems to support the position that the primary and overriding purpose of all the miracles of the New Testament was to validate God's presence and action through His Son and His Apostles.

Another observation from these New Testament passages is that physical healing and spiritual healing may occur separately or together. Such independent healing is consistent with the Biblical understanding that body and soul (spirit) are separate entities.

Disease and Sickness in the New Testament

Asthenes. Derivations of this stem occur eighty-six times in the New Testament, but they are rarely used with an identifiable physical problem (John 5:5; II Corinthians 12:5, 9; Galatians 4:13). In all but two instances associated with disease (John 5:5, 7; Acts 4:9), the word designates a condition that is life-threatening: Lazarus (John 11:1, 2, 3, 4, 6), Epaphroditus (Philippians 2:20, 27), a boy with fever (John 4:47), and Tabitha (Acts 9:37). Most contexts where this root occurs involve healing in a generic sense (Matthew 10:8, Luke 10:9; and Acts 5:15, 16). Thus, its primary use with reference to disease connotes either a life-threatening severity or generic acts of healing.

Most uses reflect various types of weaknesses, e.g., of the conscience (I Corinthians 8:7, 9, 10, 11, 12), of the flesh (Matthew 26:41; Mark 14:38), of physical appearance (I Corinthians 2:3; II Corinthians 2:3), of the inability of the commandments to save (Hebrew 7:18), and of the wife as the weaker vessel (I Peter 3:7). Further, it is contrasted to strength, e.g., between God and men (I Corinthians 1:25), between the earthly and the resurrected body (I Corinthians 15:43), and between believers (I Corinthians 4:10, 12:22; II Corinthians 13:3; I Thessalonians 5:14). Thus, *asthenes* has a wide variety of uses.

Asthenes is another word that may identify either the physical or spiritual components of man according to its use in context. This two-fold use further identifies that sickness may reside in man's body, his spirit (soul), or both.

Nosos. From this root, the word "nosology" (the classification of diseases) is derived. Derivations of this stem are used fourteen times in the New Testament. In every instance except two, it is used of generic healing: Matthew 4:24; Mark 1:34; Luke 6:17; and Acts 19:12. One exception may be the healing performed by an angel at the Bethesda pool. In another exception, *nosos* indicates an excessive interest in controversy and disputes (NASB, "morbid"). *Nosos*, however, never refers to identifiable physical problems.

Arrhostos. Five occurrences are found in the New Testament, but it does not specifically refer to identifiable disease, either. Two passages are noteworthy. In I Corinthians 11:30, *arrhostos* ("sick") is the result, even to death, of judgment for participation in the Lord's Supper in an "unworthy manner." In Mark 6:13, the twelve were sent out to anoint people who were *arrhostos*.

Kakos. The derivations of this stem in the New Testament predominantly refer to that which is evil or destructive. For our concern, it is used of physical injury in Acts 16:28 and 28:5. Its compound form, *kakopatheo*, relates to suffering and hardship (John 5:10, 13; II Timothy 2:9, and II Timothy 4:5). Paired with *echo* (to have), it mostly connotes generic healing as in Matthew 14:35 and Mark 1:32, 34. It does denote, however, the specific problem of the centurion's servant (Luke 7:2). Further, Christ made the analogy that He came to those who were "sick" (Matthew 9:12; Mark 2:17; Luke 5:31).

Kamno. Only three times does this word appear in the New Testament. In Hebrews 12:13 and Revelation 2:3, it means the opposite of endurance and perseverance. In James 5:15, it designates those upon whom the prayer of faith is effectual.

Malakia. All three occurrences are used to name those who were healed generically.

Adunatos, "inability," contrasts with *dunatos* ("power" or "ability" - Matthew 6:13 and "miracle" - Mark 9:39). In Acts 14:8, the lame man was "without strength" in his feet.

Miscellaneous. The Greek words which refer to specific physical disorders, e.g., *cholos* (lame) or *paralutikos* (paralysis), are not considered. Such specific entities are necessary only to demonstrate that healings were physical (organic) in nature. The purpose of this review is to examine the *means* by which healing occurred.

Naos, hieron. These words are both translated *temple*. The former, however, is used to denote a particular part of the Temple, the Holy of Holies, where the priest entered only once each year (Hebrews 9:1-7). The latter refers to the entire building or its parts, as distinct from the inner sanctuary. Further, *naos* refers to the fleshly body of Christ (John 2:19, 20, 21) and the body of the believer (I Corinthians 6:19). Thus, the physical body, as it is indwelt by God the Holy Spirit, is identified with the Holy of Holies.

Oinos. Wine was suggested to Timothy (I Timothy 5:23) to use for his stomach and frequent illnesses (*asthenes*) and was used by the Good Samaritan (Luke 10:34). Thus, in the New Testament, this one substance (wine) is used medicinally both internally and externally. In the first instance, its medical value is not clear, although Paul may have suggested wine to Timothy to stimulate his appetite or to quiet his anxiety, since Timothy was young and timid and faced huge responsibilities. A possible physical manifestation of such anxiety is a poor appetite. The wine could have been used for both these reasons, causing Timothy to relax enough to eat and overcome his weakened condition (*asthenes*).

Of course, even this explanation is conjectural, and its recommendation came, not from a physician, but an Apostle. Since the Bible warns repeatedly of the dangers of alcohol (Proverbs 23:20-21, 29-35; Ephesians 5:18), Timothy was specifically instructed to use a *little* (*oligos*) wine! In the case of the Samaritan, alcohol does have antiseptic (bacteria-killing properties, which made its use appropriate in open wounds.

These two situations demonstrate recommended (Timothy) and applied (the Good Samaritan) uses of wine which are consistent with some known medical properties. Although physicians were not involved, these passages record the moral use of wine (a drug) for physical symptoms and injury.

Elaion. Twice oil was used to anoint the sick: *asthenes* (James 5:14) and *arrhostos* (Mark 6:13), although an identifiable physical problem was not named. The Good Samaritan applied oil, as well as wine, to the beaten man's wounds, but in this instance, medical knowledge is not helpful. Olive and other oils may be used to soften and prevent skin from drying, but are currently thought to be contraindicated where the skin is broken, particularly burned, and likely to increase the incidence of infection. Of course, medical science changes and remains incomplete. It is inconceivable that Christ would have told a parable that included an injurious mode of treatment.

Conclusion

Can any principles, relative to physicians and their practices, be derived from this overview of New Testament terminology? Definitively, the texts which involve oil and wine seem to allow for the use of both internal and external applications of medications. It is interesting that neither is applied or directed by a physician. Further, no explicit or implicit didactic or historical passage in the entire Bible refers to a specific example of healing by a physician.

The only explicit direction to believers concerning sickness is James 5:13-18. From this passage some theologians have concluded that anointing with oil (a medicine) may be interpreted to allow for the various treatments of physicians. In a personal review of conservative commentaries on this passage, interpretations were varied, inconsistent, and even contradictory. Without consistent agreement, it would seem tenuous and unreasonable to vary from a literal interpretation, i.e., a simple application by elders in conjunction with possible confession and repentance. Thus, an ethic for the relationship of physicians and believers must be established from other Biblical principles, since no directly applicable texts offer explicit or clearly implicit instruction.

Note to readers: This Appendix was taken from Chapter 7 of my book *Biblical/Medical Ethics*. The only change from the original is some minor editing.

Notes and References

1. Even though the believer under grace is no longer bound by the ceremonial law, current empirical evidence defines what could not be otherwise: what is spiritually healthy through the ceremonial law is physically healthy, as well, since man is a physical and spiritual unity.

2. This study was a fascinating process, because the Holy Spirit wrote many passages in such a manner as to define both the process of healing and the specific physical problems by context without dependence of the interpretation upon lexicons.

Young's Analytical Concordance and *Vine's Expository Dictionary of New Testament Words* were used to locate the pertinent words which follow. These two sources are referenced to the King James Version of the Bible, but quotations are from the New American Standard Bible in this Appendix. The Greek stems (in parenthesis) were referenced in *Young's* to locate the various Bible passages where they occurred. This procedure prevents an inadvertent omission of a Greek word which has an unexpected English translation.

3. John Calvin, *Commentary on a Harmony of the Evangelists* (reprint edition, Grand Rapids: Baker Book House, 1979), pp. 231-232.

4. W. H. Hobart, *The Medical Language of St. Luke* (Dublin: Hodges, Figgis, and Co., 1882), p. 295.

A Special Message to
Physicians and Medical Students

My involvement in medical education began in 1965, my freshman year of medical school, and continues to the present (excluding three years of military service). This period includes four years of medical school, one of internship, two years of family practice residency, and almost 20 years on the faculty of the Medical College of Georgia. I have observed the lives of peers and other students from their own entry into medical school, through residency training, and eventually into private practice or academia. A common pattern with many Christian medical students has been an increasing involvement in medicine and a decreasing involvement with other areas of Christian responsibility, including a weak Biblical worldview.

Medical school begins after four years of college and consists of four additional years. Specialty training (residency) is another three to seven years. By then, most physicians are approximately thirty years of age and, since the age of six, have been in formal education. Still ahead is a practice to be established or academic recognition to be achieved. The whole process is arduous and demanding. Little time is available for a serious reflection upon the totality of one's life.[1]

To graduate from college with an intact Biblical faith is in itself an achievement because of the secular bombardment in most colleges. Even so, many do survive with their faith intact. Others actually make a profession of faith during those trying years.

In medical school, however, the above-mentioned pattern begins. The first two years of medical school are similar to college with its regularity of class structure, so Christian students often remain active in their churches and Christian organizations on campus.

As clinical training with patients (in most institutions) begins during the third and fourth years, however, the students appear less frequently in Christian contexts. Most are irregularly active or entirely absent. Days are filled with rounds, workups, laboratory studies, conferences, and other aspects of patient care. Nights involve on-call duty. Neither their churches nor campus fellowships, however, show much concern, because these students are involved in a high calling of service to mankind, *the practice of medicine*! Unfortunately, too many of them continue in this pattern for the rest of their lives, as they allow their professional duties to exclude spiritual obligations.

Developing Biblical Priorities

Medicine is a high calling, but it must be placed within a Biblical system of priorities. That is, medicine must be placed within the whole will of God. The believer must seek Biblical responsibilities in *every* area of his life for his own spiritual growth and his ministry to others.

We saw in Chapters 1 and 2 that optimal physical health is promoted by a right relationship and obedience to the Great Physician. On this basis, the inclusion of spiritual activities, e.g., prayer, evangelism, and counseling, is an essential ingredient of a Biblical medical practice.

Not only must God's commands be followed because He is God, but His way (will) always has the best results for all concerned (physical health being no exception). *"For what will a man be profited, if he gains the whole world and forfeits his soul? (Matthew 16:26).*[2] A specific application of this verse could be, "What will a physician be profited if he is a great physician in every other way except the establishment of God's will in his practice -- to the neglect of his own soul and that of his patients?"

Too many Christians are confused about the "will of God." Often, the phrase is equated with a young person's choice of a career. Certainly, the will of God includes a career, but a career is in reality only a small a part of the whole. In fact, if a Christian does not seek to practice the whole of God's will, he is less likely to choose the best career for serving God! Garry Friesen has written a very practical book concerning the will of God that every believer should read.[3]

God's will for the believer is synonymous with those activities which govern one's relationship to God and others, as prescribed in the Bible. While these activities may be categorized in various ways, I will present here some direction from what has been helpful to my own life and in counseling. It may give a practical "handle" to some who have not yet organized their own spiritual lives.

First, there are four personal *characteristics* that each Christian should develop in his own life. These are *certainty of salvation* (an understanding of justification by faith), *right* (submissive) *attitude, obedience* (in attitude and activities), and *perseverance* (a persistence through times of trial and peace).

Nine *activities* of the Christian life are worship, prayer, Bible study, personal ministry (marriage and the local church), maintenance of physical health, fellowship, mortification (a putting to death) of sin, and daily necessities (the "mundane," e.g., eating, taking a shower, getting dressed, etc.). I will discuss some of these and leave others for readers' own investigation and study.

I have found the study of time management to be beneficial in helping set Biblical priorities. The goal is adequate time to engage in these activities in a quality way through an organized, planned schedule. Businesses do not function smoothly without schedules, and neither will individual lives. A sobering thought is the realization that *we are most likely reach those goals which we truly value.* Thus, our daily activities *clearly reveal what we truly value.*

Worship, Prayer, and Bible Study

Worship, prayer, and Bible study are the most direct means by which a believer relates to God. *Worship* should be both corporate (Hebrew 10:25) and personal (Matthew 6:9-10;

Psalm 1:2). *Prayer* includes worship (Matthew 6:9-10), confession (I John 1:9), and thanksgiving and supplication (Philippians 4:6). The importance of the devotional time is recognized by most Christians, but the need for its *daily, quality* observance often is overlooked (Psalms 1:2, 5:3; Luke 9:23; Matthew 6:34). The best time is early morning (Psalm 5:3; Psalm 57:8; Matthew 6:1; and Luke 4:42).

Bible study, as meditation, should be a part of the devotional time, but it should be pursued *systematically* and vigorously at other times on an ongoing basis. Spiritual growth is dependent upon Biblical knowledge, understanding, and application, which come only through diligent effort. The New Testament is clear about this effort when it uses such words as "work," "discipline," "disciple," "slave," "armor," "wrestle," "diligent," "persevere," and "strive."

I am convinced that the lack of study and practical application of the Bible are the major reasons for the defeated and impotent lives of individual Christians and the universal (true) Church. The moral consciousness of the believer is little, if any, better without the light of Scripture than that of the unbeliever. *I issue a challenge to the Christian physician to study the Bible with the same diligence and effort that he studies medicine.* I am convinced that your care of patients will only be enhanced as God redeems the time that you as a physician give to God's priorities.

The Bible is not easy to study, but many excellent tapes, books, seminars, courses, and other means are available to assist the Christian. Concurrently, skills for personal study of the Bible should be developed as one studies the interpretation and teaching of others. Professional and personal ethics especially should be the fruit of such study, as God *"has granted to us everything pertaining to life and godliness" (II Peter 1:3).*

Ministry: First to Marriage and Family

The concept of "ministry" has several applications. Physicians and medical students should not overlook their responsibilities to their spouses, children, and local churches, as well as to their profession. God designed marriage to reflect the relationship within the Trinity (I Corinthians 11:3), with the husband loving his wife as "Christ also loved the church" (Ephesians 5:25).

The responsibility for love in the home does not fall on the wife, but on the husband.[4] On the other side, if the wife is the physician, she is still to be subject to her husband, "as to the Lord" (Ephesians 5:22). The professional role of either spouse must not interfere with marriage responsibilities. For example, neither the husband's not the wife's body belongs to himself or herself, but each belongs to the other (I Corinthians 7:3-5).

From the beginning (Genesis 2:18), the unity of husband and wife ("one flesh," Genesis 2:24; Matthew 19:5) has been the basic building block of the church and society (except for those individuals who have the gift of celibacy) (I Corinthians 7:7). *Leadership in the church is based on qualities of leadership in the home* (I Timothy 3:4-5).

Thus, the Biblical priority within the home is the marital relationship, not the parent-child relationship. Children, however, are not to be neglected but are to be brought "up in the discipline and instruction of the Lord" (Ephesians 6:4), as a way of life (Deuteronomy 6:4-9). Certainly, this plan requires a significant effort by the parents.

Practically, the husband (or the wife) who is a physician must be certain that time is scheduled (not left to chance) for his/her spouse and their children. This scheduling will require *complete* call-coverage by other physicians and specific hours for patient care. Irregular and interrupted schedules can be devastating to family relationships. The priority of a physician's practice over his family is frequently where he fails Biblically.

Patient care should not prevent responsibilities to wife and children. Actually, neither has to exclude the other. An accurate barometer to determine whether the quality and quantity of time at home are adequate for both the spouse and the children may be the non-physician spouse. *Ask him or her frequently for an evaluation of how you are doing! The physician-spouse is not able to accurately make that determination.*

There is no Biblical basis that allows neglect of the home, even for the care of patients. No doubt, scheduling spouse and

family time will be difficult with the demands of medical practice, but many Christian physicians have been able to achieve
this balance. This priority is so important that changes in practice arrangements, e.g., off-duty coverage, geographical loca-
tion, and even partners, should be made to allow for family
time. If the neglect of the spouse (first) and the children
(second) does happen, the physician has made primary what
should be secondary. Even worse, that choice involves continuing sin because of its improper balance.

Ministry: Outside the Family and to the Church

Another area of ministry that should not be neglected is the
local church. Every Christian is a part of the body of Christ
(Romans 12:5; I Corinthians 12:1-7). The primary expression
of this relationship is the local church, where *every member* has
an essential role for his own maturity in Christ, as well as that
of the church body (Ephesians 4:11-16). Gifts are given for the
numerical and spiritual growth of the church body, not for
one's career (Ephesians 4:12).

Believers have a special obligation to other believers, an
obligation that they do not have to unbelievers (Galatians 6:10).
A specific point of conflict may be Sunday. Obviously, patient
care must continue seven days a week, but the physician who
realizes that Sunday has been ordained by God as a day of
worship and rest (Exodus 20:9-11) will make rounds and
schedule his calls to allow for active participation in his church
on this special day.

Physical Health and Spiritual Commitment

An activity to which all Christians are Biblically directed,
but one which physicians should personally emphasize, is that
of maintaining physical health (I Corinthians 3:16-17, 6:19).
This activity is a special opportunity for the physician to
demonstrate, by his example, maintenance and preventive care
to his patients. The omission of such efforts implies that after-
the-fact medical care is more important than health maintenance
and disease prevention. Role modeling is probably the strong-

est means of teaching (Mark 3:14; Luke 6:40; Acts 4:13). Paul was not afraid, nor was he boastful, in pointing to himself as an example (Philippians 3:17; II Thessalonians 3:7) and directing others to be an example (I Timothy 4:12).

Fellowship, mortification (the process of putting off sin that is progressive but never completed in this earthly life), and daily necessities will be left to readers' own investigation and study. You are encouraged to read other books and articles about personal Christian ethics, a number of which are referenced in this book. Only by the renewing of our minds will our lives and practices be transformed according to God's will, rather than be conformed to the world's life and practice.

These activities, as patterns in one's life, should be developed as early as possible. Medical school or residency training does not exempt one from these Biblically prescribed activities. Jesus said that His followers must count the cost. For the physician, this cost may include less income, fewer patients, less availability to patients, and possibly, a lesser standing among peers. The medical student may sacrifice better grades, and from that, less chance of acceptance into the more prestigious residency programs.

To the medical student or physician, however, who chooses God's ways and means, *"If God is for us, who is against us? He who did not spare His own Son, but delivered Him up for us all, how will He not also with Him freely give us all things?" (Romans 8:31-32).* Initially, these things may appear to be sacrifices, but in reality they are only our "reasonable service" (Romans 12:1, KJV) which is *"producing for us an eternal weight of glory far beyond all comparison (II Corinthians 4:17).* Even now, in this life, peace and joy are promised (Romans 5:1; James 1:2-4).

The central issue is *priority.* No profession or vocation is so important that it may supersede those activities to which every Christian is directed by the Scriptures.[5] The important role of medical care that has been ascribed by society and exists within the medical profession tends to blur God's priorities. Until Christian physicians rearrange their priorities, a clear and progressive understanding of the modern relationship of medicine and the Christian faith is not likely to occur. Worse, preoccupation with medicine can become excessive, even to the point where one violates the First Commandment (Exodus 20:3; Matthew 22:37-38). Some physicians might object to these directives on the grounds that their burdened lives will be further burdened. But they must be reminded that God never places more responsibilities upon us than those which can be competently managed (I Corinthians 10:13; James 1:2-4). When demands are excessive, we have placed them upon ourselves (Proverbs 14:12).

Evangelism

> "The physician cannot take advantage of the vulnerability of the sick patient to advance his own, or even his nation's social and political philosophy. This is a first principle derived from the fact of illness, the act of profession, the principle of non-harm, and the ethical axiom of vulnerability."[6]

> "...It needs to be said again and again, that the doctor's task is first and last, and all along, to be a good doctor -- not an evangelist."[7]

> "To argue that people should be left to their original religions reveals both disbelief in the historic Christian claim to be the only true religion and a fundamental misunderstanding of evangelism."[8]

Should physicians evangelize their patients? As noted above, ethicists disagree. Abuses in evangelism in medical settings do occur. Dr. Pellegrino points that physical illness makes a patient vulnerable. Dr. Vale emphasizes the medical role of the physician. However, the command is *"Go and make disciples of all nations" (Matthew 28:18)*. Thus, Dr. Tinder has the Biblical perspective. *The Christian physician cannot exclude evangelism from his practice.*

At the same time, the Christian physician must not coerce patients who are "off their guard" because of their medical concerns. Time and place of evangelism are important factors, and the physician should not persist if the patient, verbally or nonverbally, indicates disinterest or opposition. (In today's anti-Christian legal environment, such persistence could even result in a lawsuit!)

Medical needs, as one kind of physical need, offer an opportunity to evangelize (James 2:15-18). Further, as I have shown earlier, spiritual health is a prerequisite to physical health. Thus, *evangelism is essential to good medicine.*

Are patients willing to hear the Gospel? My own experience and that of colleagues is that patients are quite willing to hear the Gospel. However, they are often not willing to act on that information, as their minds seem set for a "physical" cure. But, is that situation any different from any other evangelistic opportunity? We are to "be ready in season and out of season" (II Timothy 4:2). Some "plant," others "water," and God causes the "increase" (I Corinthians 3:6).

For sure, medical situations are opportunities when patients realize their vulnerability and may reflect more deeply upon their eternal destinies. We need to take appropriate advantage of these situations.

The physician who is going to evangelize and counsel patients Biblically should probably inform his patients of this intent when they first enter his practice. He does not have to inform them personally, but may give them a letter describing how his practice is "different" from those of most physicians. While many patients will not remember this information, at least the physician will be able to refer back to it, should the need ever arise.

Does evangelism involve deception, since the patient comes to the physician for medical help? Obviously, the content of this book answers that question. Medical problems have been shown to be related directly and indirectly to spiritual problems. For example, treatment of the cause of the problem may be unavoidably spiritual, as in a sexually transmitted disease.

Two factors do limit physicians' opportunities to evangelize their patients. First, patients have a high expectation for a medical solution which is quick and complete, as this attitude is enhanced by the media. Failure to realize this expectation may cause patients to lose respect and trust in their physicians.

Second, the Holy Spirit prepares people to receive spiritual truth. Even though most patients will listen politely, many will not respond. Others will respond purely in the hope that somehow their physical condition will be helped.[9] The physician needs to clearly understand the Spirit's role. As finite beings, we cannot discern the openness of another's heart. We are only His instruments to present the Gospel, but God has promised that His Word will not return empty (Isaiah 55:11). Many patients will not accept the truth, but some will, so opportunities must be seized.

A case from my early practice illustrates how the Spirit may work over time. I had been providing medical care to Tom and Mary and their two children for three years when Tom hit Mary with his fist one night during one of their frequent arguments. She came for counseling, but he was unwilling to come, even though he had professed a conversion experience several months earlier.

I was frustrated. How could I encourage his wife, an unbeliever, to submit to her husband and love him in light of such physical abuse? After a few sessions, I presented the Gospel, and she trusted Christ. About the same time, Tom began to come for counseling, but he was still rebellious concerning any change. Gradually, they became influenced by a Pentecostal community, learned Biblical roles in marriage, and began to practice them. This change occurred more than 15 years ago and has only grown since that time! The final outcome did not develop clearly or predictably, yet the Spirit was at work and even harmonized the efforts of believers of different persuasions.

How evangelism is practiced by each physician will vary. Christians have different spiritual gifts (Romans 12:6-8; I Corinthians 12-14; Ephesians 4:8-13; and I Peter 4:10-11). Some will have the gift of evangelism. Another will have teaching gifts. Obviously, then, what each Christian does will depend largely upon his gifts.

To allow time for evangelism and/or other spiritual ministry to patients, the physician will have to structure the time into his practice. Solutions might include making specific appointments that allow more time with these patients or even setting aside one-half day a week when only these patients are seen.

A plan should be devised to provide an opportunity for every patient to hear the Gospel. Office personnel may be assigned this function. Christians who have been through a similar circumstance that the patient is experiencing may be used to establish identity and may be even more effective. Literature may be made available in the waiting room. Mailings allow for contact with every patient.

To personalize his witness, the physician could write a brief summary of his own conversion and the importance of Christ in his life and publish it for distribution to his patients. In this way, he could make himself vulnerable, as the patient is vulnerable. As someone has said, "Witnessing is one beggar telling another where to find bread." Physicians need to be open, as patients are open. A spiritual history could be included as a part of the medical history. One ophthalmologist has devised eye charts which contain lines of a simple Gospel tract! With some time for creative thought, a physician could make evangelism a natural part of his medical practice.

The Physician and His Practice

For some Christians, a dichotomy exists between the spiritual and the secular realms. Physicians must be careful that they do not separate their medical practices from their Christian beliefs. Jesus prayed, *"I do not ask Thee to take them out of the world, but to keep them from the evil one" (John 17:15)*. Paul directed, *"Whatever you do, do your work heartily as for the Lord rather than for men...It is the Lord Christ whom you serve" (Colossians 3:23-24)*. Under His Lordship, no one area of life is competitive with another.

Denis Burkitt, famous in the medical world for his work with the type of cancer (lymphoma) that carries his name, reflected on his experience.

"I find my attention...is directed to increasingly costly, and to a lesser degree increasingly successful, provisions made and measures adopted, to cater to the physical needs of the biological component of man (p.

4). Even on a purely scientific level we have probably grossly over-estimated the achievement of medical science, yet when one considers man in his true proportions, it is humbling to realize (and more so to acknowledge) how relatively little we have benefited many of our patients...to consider Christ's challenging question 'What is a man profited even though he gains the whole world and loses himself?...' To what extent do I profit my patients or others if I treat them exceedingly well; but do nothing whatever to improve the welfare of their true selves? (p. 12). With all its credible achievements, the overscientific approach to medicine can easily turn pathetic patients into consecutive cases, and care-ridden mothers into clinical material" (p. 5).

"So often our patients have a problem that is not removable and sometimes only slightly alleviable. In those circumstances the all-important factor is the ability to accept and even triumph by the aid of inward resources" (p. 15).[10]

In his concluding remarks to this address, Dr. Burkitt presented the example of the man in Jesus' parable who lived a "totally biologically-oriented life" (Luke 16:19-31). His food, his clothes, and his home bore eloquent testimony to his priorities. He asked for, but was not granted, a return to physical existence to warn others. His message "would have been a plea to concentrate on the spiritual, to take earnest regard to their standing before God and their eternal well being."[11] In all the technology and sophistication of modern medicine, are Christian physicians too concerned with the limited existence of the physical body compared to the immortal soul?

The Christian physician's goal should be to determine how success is defined.[12] A sobering thought in this regard is the reality that ultimately we will fail with every patient: He or she will die. This point is obvious, but how many medical students and physicians ever seriously ponder this fact? How is ultimate failure reconciled with successful medicine? To what extent should the physician blame himself each time his patients die?

With every patient, the greatest wisdom and technology that medical science can offer, at some point, will fail.

Perhaps, the physician should meditate in his "quiet time" about the situations in his life about which Jesus might say, *"Well done, thou good and faithful servant" (Matthew 25:23, KJV).*

There are simple things that students and physicians can do. The physician should be careful to think of patients as people and to call them by their names.[13] An expression such as "the cirrhotic in room 212" denotes a disease entity and not a person with an immortal soul. Words such as "crock," "troll," "dirtball," "gomer," and "spos" ("disposable") are common expressions that are heard and repeated from a medical student's early experience on the wards. Patients are labeled "interesting" if they have some disease process or finding which is unusual or represents a good example for teaching purposes.

The physician may seek opportunities to pray with his patients, especially during times of severe illness or major surgery. Many patients who are not believers cherish prayer, and it may open an opportunity for the physician to present the Gospel. Perhaps, the introductory letter to patients (mentioned above) could let patients know that you are available to pray with them.

God's sovereignty can be a great comfort to the believing physician. A simple, but not simplistic, summary of the concept is *"And we know that God causes all things to work together for good to those who love God, to those who are called according to His purpose" (Romans 8:28).* Any reader not fully acquainted with God's sovereignty should study the concept. The Westminster Confession of Faith, for example, discusses God's plans and purposes in a full and complete way. For example, the threat of malpractice causes some physicians to order "tests" that might otherwise not be done. The Christian physician does not have to be subject to this pressure. He is free to exercise his best judgment and rest upon God's sovereignty whenever he has managed the patient to the best of his ability, realizing his finite knowledge and skills. Then, any complications or unexpected events are within God's will.

God's sovereignty is not an excuse for incompetent medical

care, obviously, but it does guarantee freedom for the physician to rest the patient's outcome with the Great Physician. The unbeliever faces the stark reality that his own fallibility is the only hope he has to offer his patient. No wonder the suicide rate for physicians is one of the highest of any profession!

Physicians face temptations which are unique to their profession.[14]

1) Financial prosperity is essentially guaranteed, but the Scriptures are clear that riches present one of the major temptations to be overcome (Matthew 6:19-24, 13:22, 19:23, 24; I Timothy 6:6-10).

2) Sexual problems head almost every New Testament listing of sins (Matthew 5:28; Mark 7:20-23; Galatians 5:19-21; Colossians 3:5-11). The physician is privileged to examine the naked body and must be careful to minimize temptation.

3) Pride results from the prestige and status that society bestows upon the physician (Proverbs 16:8; James 4:6; I Peter 5:5; I John 2:16).

4) The care of patients during the night is exhausting, so sufficient rest must be planned following those times (Psalm 127:2).

5) Drugs which relieve pain and tension are accessible, making the physician vulnerable to self-medication.

6) Patients' demands which abuse a physician's time, and professional peer pressure are other problems.

Other specifics might be named, but these are sufficient to indicate the severity and constancy of temptation for the Christian physician who carries the defeated, but still-present, old nature (Romans 6:1-23, 7:14-25). If the above or other temptations result in sin (James 1:13-15), guilt occurs.

Sadly, too many Christians do not understand how God has provided for guilt. "Where the guilt complex remains, it paralyzes moral effort.[15] Much more could be said here, but three basic principles may suffice to overcome guilt.

The first principle is justification by faith. If one does not understand the fullness and finality of forgiveness and purity in a relationship with God through Jesus Christ, he is impotent to progress in the Christian life and to experience joy and peace. A detailed study of Romans 1-8 is a must for this understanding.

Second, the burden of guilt is unnecessary for the Christian (Romans 8:1). Christ provided forgiveness of sins through His blood sacrifice (Hebrews 9:22). *"If we confess our sins, he is faithful and just to forgive us our sins, and to cleanse us from all unrighteousness" (I John 1:9, NKJV).* His great sacrifice and our commitment to repentance removes the spiritual reality of guilt. Feelings of remorse, sadness, and shame may persist, but right thinking and right action will markedly diminish them over time.

Third, repetitive ("besetting sins") are the most crippling because of cumulative guilt feelings. For the reader who continues to be frustrated and burdened by guilt, Dr. Jay Adams has thoroughly developed the Biblical concepts of guilt and forgiveness.[16] In another book, he has detailed the practical application of those concepts.[17] A balanced, effective understanding cannot be accomplished without *serious* study and meditation, but the Christian life is intended by its Creator to be a life of joy, peace, and growth in righteousness. Any Christian who is not experiencing these should further examine his entire understanding of his relationship to God, the freedom to activity which flows from the relationship, and the power to overcome sin.

Physicians are sometimes unaware of their biases, as they are taught to be "objective" with patients. That goal is desirable, but it is impossible to put into practice. In particular, Christians should, as they mature, become increasingly aware of the deceitfulness of their own hearts (Jeremiah 17:9). In managing patients, the physician's and the patient's attitudes and biases should be kept in mind by both:

> "On the one hand, consider the physician with an aggressively interventionist philosophy.... In situations that could be expected to improve spontaneously, intervention would nevertheless be undertaken to promote a more rapid or comfortable return to health.... On the other hand, consider the more passive physician with a non-interventionist approach.... This physician would view the body as a sort of sacred entity that should be

manipulated only under exceptional circumstances.[18]

For example, surgery for atherosclerosis of the cerebral (brain) arteries remains highly controversial. The "interventionist" physician would urge the patient to have surgery, whereas the "non-interventionist" physician would direct his patients *not* to have surgery. The patient could not avoid being influenced by the physician's medical judgment and would probably never be aware of the equivocal nature of the surgery in either case.

Another example demonstrates *patient bias*. Healthy volunteers were placed in the circumstance of having cancer of the larynx.[19] Their choices were: (1) laryngectomy (removal of the larynx) with a three-year survival rate of 60 percent, or (2) radiation therapy, with a 30-40 percent three-year survival. One out of five chose radiation with its lesser longevity in order to preserve their voices. Such choices are not predictable, so there must be effective communication between patient and physician.

The respect, and often awe, with which patients may view their physicians is powerful and often inhibits them from freely expressing themselves.[20] The physician needs to develop a conscious awareness of this attitude as well as his own biases as he explores values with his patients. Medical decisions involve much subjectivity by both patient and physician as these two examples (above) illustrate. The patient's best interest will be reached more likely by reciprocal communication.

The Christian physician should consider other modifications of his practice with patients. The resources of the Christian (counseling, prayer, anointing, spiritual strengthening, and the local community of believers) are much greater than those of the non-Christian. The Christian physician should strive to develop those resources. Some may be available through contacts with the patient's pastor and/or church. Many Christian patients are already aware of these resources.

This situation is strategic! Because many liberal and conservative churches fail to teach the strengths available to the believer, the physician can counsel the patient or direct him to a pastor who can counsel. Floundering Christians, then, will have an opportunity to experience the fullness of "body life" through these spiritual resources and then to contribute themselves to the advancement of the Kingdom.

Christian patients may *cause* particular problems for physicians. For example, their views on healing may differ from those of the physician, resulting in a conflict. Lengthy explanations may be necessary to explain why healing did not occur, even though the ritual of their particular fellowship was carried out. Expectations of a Christian physician may exceed his resources, ability, or may even be impossible to meet. A simple, quick remedy may be expected when a lengthy, persevering process is the only alternative. As in counseling, three questions will help to clarify patients' expectations. 1) "What is your problem?" 2) "What have you done about it?" 3) "What do you want *me* to do about it?"[21] Even with these problems, however, most Christian patients are enjoyable to work with, knowing that we share the same general approach to life and health.

Primary care physicians (family physicians, pediatricians, obstetrician-gynecologists, and general internists) who desire a truly Christian practice may face serious financial limitations. The practices described here involve more time with some patients and considerable time away from medical practice to fulfill the "balanced" life. One physician whom I know personally has limited his practice for these reasons, and the respect he has from other physicians has resulted in their referral of themselves and their families to him.

Even further restrictions may occur if Biblical evaluation of the "third-party" payer concept (private insurance, industrial, and governmental programs) reveals that this removal of primary responsibility from the patient is inconsistent with Biblical accountability. Another physician of whom I am aware is convinced that such payment is unbiblical and has established his practice on that basis. He *has* had considerably less income than most physicians in situations similar to his own. This result reflects the cost of commitment (Luke 14:24-35) to *distinctive* Christian principles. His example should stimulate others in the profession to such commitment.

In summary, the Christian physician should help his patients aim toward spiritual goals, realizing their tendency toward preoccupation with the physical body. He should reflect seriously upon the balance between caring, curing, and the ultimate death of every patient. Euphemisms relating to patients should be avoided. Prayer should be a natural response with patients. The physician's fallibility rests in God's sovereignty. Temptations must be avoided, but where conscious sin occurs, a clear understanding of guilt, forgiveness, and change can be sought. Although objectivity in medical decisions is a reasonable goal, the impossibility of achieving it should be recognized. Practical use of the resources of Christian patients may enhance or impede care. These beliefs may be obtained during the patient history. Other distinctives may be developed by the thinking Christian physician.

Some Words to the Medical Student

"Having survived the premedical grind, the vast majority (of medical students) genuinely desire to be helpers. As they spend more of their waking hours in classroom, laboratory, and later in high pressure clinical settings among patients who are in and out of the hospital and whom they can only marginally help, they set aside... their own humanity to learn the science and technology of medicine. In a sense they cultivate a persona that is more professionalized and narrowed. In so doing, there is a danger of becoming "we" not "they" --the people served...In the process insidious changes in personality may occur."[22]

This description and the one which began this chapter should raise red flags or warnings to medical students.

The time for the Christian to develop right patterns of life is *now*. Pressures will *increase* over the next several years with further training and the likelihood of a family. A tendency of the sinful nature is to think that the future somehow will be more manageable than the present. Such deception is common, since the physician has many "wait-untils" (graduation, residency, practice, etc.). The medical student who cannot manage the Biblical priorities that have been briefly presented will find that changes become increasingly difficult the further he goes in his medical career. He may even want to consider another career that has less demands.

Consider going to Bible college or seminary. Probably, the easiest time to pursue any formal training is the earlier period of adult life when a family is not yet established, the habits of study are familiar, and one is already adjusted to a lower level of income. An opportune time is upon completion of an internship and prior to specialization. The physician can obtain a state license to allow necessary income to be earned with only a few hours per week of "moonlighting."

Also, this juncture allows further evaluation of future plans, including the possibility of missionary service, since the greatest need for medical care remains in the Third World countries. The medical problems of the Western world are primarily of a direct spiritual nature, but other countries lack basic medicine and hygiene. No doubt, the physician who truly desires to be most effective in medical care will consider Third World needs.

The Christian medical student needs to consider seriously that in many instances, a truly Christian medical practice will not yield the income that other physicians receive. He must be careful to avoid the attitude that he has a right to a large income. Biblically, the lure of money is a frequent cause of compromise of principle. By developing clear principles for a practice and an expectancy of less income, the temptation for compromise will be much decreased.

A special plea is made to the medical student or young physician who is interested in the fullest development and definition of a Biblical approach to medical care. He should seriously consider a full seminary education, with the inclusion of Greek and Hebrew. Not only is a much greater development in Biblical/medical ethics needed, but the study of the Biblical words that describe diseases, treatment, and other medically related matters is needed.

The understanding of these words could be enriched by a comparison of the historical usage with modern concepts of human physiology. Perhaps, such a physician would be able to assist translators. An example is the word *leprosy* (Hebrew --

tsaraath, and Greek -- *lepra*). The modern disease known as *leprosy* constitutes only a small portion of those skin diseases which are included in the words of the original languages.[23]

The medical student must begin to think and act on Biblical priorities. God's will in all areas of the Christian life concerns much more than any career, even the practice of medicine. The diligent pursuit of a balanced Christian life will result in a more competent and caring physician than will time and energy focused almost exclusively upon the study and practice of medicine.

I offer this concluding challenge. What neither the United States nor the West needs is another physician practicing medicine in (more or less) the same way as other physicians. *What is needed are physicians willing to reform their medical practices in ways that are distinctly Biblical, no matter what the cost.* If you are unwilling to tackle the demands that such reform would require, then you should go to the mission field, where far more real physical needs are not being met.

Notes and References

1. Similar problems exist in other careers. It is a narrow perception by physicians that only we face such rigors in our professional development.

2. Except where indicated, Bible quotations in this Appendix are from the New American Standard Bible.

3. Garry Friesen, *Decision-Making and the Will of God*, (Portland, Oregon: Multnomah Press, 1980).

4. Jay E. Adams, *Christian Living in the Home* (Philadelphia: Presbyterian and Reformed Publishing Company, 1972), p. 100.

5. D. Martyn Lloyd-Jones, *The Doctor Himself and the Human Condition* (London: Christian Medical Fellowship Publications, 1982), pp. 51,63.

6. Edmund D. Pellegrino and David C. Thomasma, *A Philosophical Basis of Medical Practice* (New York: Oxford University Press, 1981), p. 275.

7. J. A. Vale, *Medicine and the Christian Mind* (London: Christian Medical Fellowship Publications, 1975), pp. 62-63.

8. Donald Tinder, "Evangelism, Ethical Aspects," in *Baker's Dictionary of Christian Ethics*, Carl F. H. Henry, ed. (Grand Rapids: Baker Book House, 1973), p. 225.

9. Lloyd-Jones, *The Doctor Himself and the Human Condition*, pp. 103ff.

10. Denis P. Burkitt, *Our Priorities* (London: Christian Medical Fellowship Publications, 1976), pp. 4-5, 12, 15.

11. *Ibid.*, p. 18.

12. Lloyd-Jones, *The Doctor Himself and the Human Condition*, pp. 12, 76ff.

13. *Ibid.*, p. 18.

14. *Ibid.*, p. 9.

15. Carl F. H. Henry, *Christian Personal Ethics* (1957; reprint ed., Grand Rapids: Baker Book House, 1977), p. 381.

16. Jay E. Adams, *More Than Redemption* (Phillipsburg, NJ: Presbyterian and Reformed Publishing Co., 1979), pp. 184-232.

17. Jay E. Adams, *The Christian Counselor's Manual* (Grand Rapids: Baker Book House, 1977), pp. 63-70.

18. A. S. Brett, "Hidden Ethical Issues in Clinical Decision Analysis," *New England Journal of Medicine* 305 (November 5, 1981), pp. 1150-1152.

19. B. J. McNeil, R. Weichselbaum, and S. G. Pauker, "Speech and Survival: Tradeoffs Between Quality and Quantity of Life in Laryngeal Cancer," *New England Journal of Medicine* 305 (October 22, 1981), pp. 982-987.

20. Lloyd-Jones, *The Doctor Himself and the Human Condition*, pp. 18, 64.

21. Adams, *The Christian Counselor's Manual*, p. 274.

22. Cato 6 (a pseudonym), "Dirtball," *Journal of the American Medical Association* 247 (June 11, 1982), pp. 3059-3060.

23. R. A. Baillie and E. E. Baillie, "Biblical Leprosy as Compared to Present Day Leprosy," *Southern Medical Journal* 75 (July 1982), pp. 855-857.

Index of Scripture

226

Index of Subjects and Proper Names

You will want your family and your church to be prepared and informed about the modern "health-care crisis"!

Do you know where to look for Biblical answers to medical and scientific dilemmas that are more frightening and complex than man has ever had to face before?

Two publications provide such answers and a forum for discussion within a Biblical worldview . . .

Journal of Biblical Ethics in Medicine

Biblical Reflections on Modern Medicine

Cost of medical care ... abortion ... euthanasia ... fetal tissue transplants ... genetic engineering ... living wills ... depression ... addiction ... contraception ... animal rights and ... many other issues are discussed regularly.

The *Journal* provides a forum for Biblical discussion -- for physicians, pastors, laymen, seminary professors, and others, but is also easily understood by the non-professional. (For more information on and how to order *Biblical Reflections on Modern Medicine*, see next page.)

The *Journal* is published four times each year. A one-year subscription is $18.00.

___ Yes, I would like to subscribe to the *Journal of Biblical Ethics in Medicine*. I have enclosed a check for $18.00 for a one-year subscription.

```
Name _____

Address _____

City, State, ZIP _____
```

Mail to: JBEM, P. O. Box 13231, Florence, SC 29504-3231.

Special discount on additional copies of this book!*

You should buy extra copies for your pastor (and the church library), your friends, physicians, and health-care workers. Please send a check, or provide charge card information below.

___ One additional copy: $10.00 (postage included).

___ 2-4 additional copies: $7.00 each (postage included).

___ 5 or more additional copies: $5.00 each (postage included).
     (Permission granted for re-sale of these books.)

And . . . for a continuing commentary on medical-ethical issues, subscribe to *Biblical Reflections on Modern Medicine*, edited by Dr. Ed Payne . . .

. . . a newsletter that is explicitly Christian and will keep you informed and educated about the ongoing and frightening issues that will affect you and your family. It is an eight-page newsletter published six times each year.

The usual price of $17.00 is <u>discounted for book purchasers</u> to <u>$10.00</u>. That's right, $7.00 off!

___ Yes, I would like to keep track of new information on medical-ethical issues with a one-year subscription to *Biblical Reflections on Modern Medicine*. I have enclosed a check for $10.00 or provided MasterCard/Visa information below.

* This page may be copied as desired by readers. Thereby, these discounts are extended to those who receive those copies.

Name _____

Address _____

City, State, ZIP _____

MasterCard or Visa No. _____ _____ _____ _____
Exp. Date ____ ____

Mail to: Covenant Enterprises, P. O. Box 14488, Augusta, GA 30919